American Medical Association

Physicians dedicated to the health of America

Mastering

the Reimbursement Process

Second Edition

L. Lamar Blount, C.P.A., F.H.F.M.A.
President
Healthcare Management Advisors, Inc.

Edward M. Mendoza, M.D., M.B.A.
Physician Consultant
Healthcare Management Advisors, Inc.

Curtis J. Udell, C.P.A.R., C.P.C.
Senior Consultant
Healthcare Management Advisors, Inc.

Joanne M. Waters, C.H.F.P.
Director, Compliance Services
Healthcare Management Advisors, Inc.

Mastering the Reimbursement Process, Second Edition

Healthcare Management Advisors, Inc. (HMA) provides education and technical support in the areas of clinical data quality, practice improvement, and regulatory compliance for physicians, hospitals, and other health care providers. HMA may be reached at www.hma.com or 770 751-1199.

Additional copies of this book may be ordered from the American Medical Association. For order information, call toll free 800 621-8335. Mention product number OP 080099.

BP48:98-1255:12M:12/98

Contents

4 Insurance Processing—Managing . . . . 95 Insurance and Patient Accounts

About the Authors

L. Lamar Blount, C.P.A., F.H.F.M.A., President During his twenty-plus years serving the health care industry, Lamar has provided and directed consulting services for more than 300 clients in thirty states. He is the president and founder of Healthcare Management Advisors, a consulting firm providing clinical data, compliance, and financial expertise to providers nationwide. He directs HMA's forty-plus person practice, which provides services in compliance programs, DRG and CPT data quality improvement, medical record and utilization reviews, and litigation support. He has served multifacility groups, as well as individual urban medical centers, rural hospitals, nursing homes, home health agencies, and physicians.

Lamar is a past president of the Georgia Rural Health Association, a fellow in the Healthcare Financial Management Association, and advisor to the Council on Finance of the Georgia Hospital Association. He is also a member of the American Institute of CPAs, the Georgia Society of CPAs, the Association of Certified Fraud Examiners, and the National Health Lawyers Association. Lamar is a certified public accountant and holds a B.B.A. from Georgia Southern University.

In addition to writing articles for various national publications, Lamar has been the publisher of HMA's *Strategy Advisor* newsletter. He has served on the editorial advisory boards for the nationally recognized *Report on Medicare Compliance*, *Hospital Payment and Information Management*, *Medical Records Briefing*, *Physician's Payment Update*, and *Medical Office Manager*. Lamar is also a frequent speaker on compliance issues, and health care financial and reimbursement topics.

Edward M. Mendoza, M.D., M.B.A., Physician Consultant Dr. Mendoza is a physician consultant for HMA and has more than twenty years of health care experience, as both a physician and a consultant. In addition to consulting with HMA, Dr. Mendoza is a clinical professor at Morehouse School of Medicine in Atlanta, directs the Geriatric and Neurology Clinics at Grady Hospital, and has a private neurology practice. Dr. Mendoza's consulting services at HMA include physician liaison training, clinical documentation quality reviews, clinical pathway development, and clinical cost management. He also assists with DRG and CPT quality reviews and educational programs for health information management, utilization management, and quality assurance personnel.

Before joining HMA, Dr. Mendoza served as associate clinical professor in neurology at the Medical College of Georgia, vice president of medical affairs for Healthshield, chief of primary care and community medicine at Eisenhower Army Medical Center, director of emergency services at St. Joseph Hospital, and chief of the neurology service at Eisenhower Army Medical Center.

Dr. Mendoza is a diplomat of the American Board of Internal Medicine, and a fellow of the American Academy of Neurology and of the American College of Physician Executives. He graduated from West Point U.S. Military Academy and received his Doctor of Medicine from Emory School of Medicine and his M.B.A. from Georgia State University.

Curtis J. Udell, C.P.A.R., C.P.C., Senior Consultant   As a senior physician reimbursement advisor at Healthcare Management Advisors, Inc., Curtis specializes in analyzing medical practice reimbursement, billing, and collection operations, establishing financial policies and procedures, and improving patient account management.

Curtis received his Bachelor of Science degree in Health Planning and Administration from Pennsylvania State University. In 1994, Curtis became a Certified Patient Account Representative, a designation awarded for knowledge in patient accounting and business office operations, and a Certified Procedure Coder.

Curtis is a sought-after lecturer to physician groups on topics such as improving evaluation and management coding, improving practice management techniques, and winning under managed care. He serves on the Editorial Advisory Board for *Physician's Marketing and Management, Briefings in Practice Management,* and the *CPA Health Niche Advisor,* and is a frequent contributor to *Medical Office Manager, Physician's Payment Update,* and *Medical Records Briefing.*

Joanne M. Waters, C.H.F.P., Director, Compliance Services   Joanne provides project management and technical support in the development of HMA's Compliance Services. In this strategic role, she uses her 15 years of experience in health care including patient financial services, diverse financial management of integrated delivery systems, medical facilities and multiphysician practice management, external and internal financial reporting, capital and operational budgeting, third-party reimbursement, managed care, and general accounting.

Before joining HMA, Joanne was director of patient financial services at Southwest Hospital and Medical Center in Atlanta. Additionally, she worked for more than 10 years in the Finance Division of South Fulton Medical Center, where she had responsibilities in both the Accounting and Patient Financial Services Departments. Periodically she was an office manager for a specialty surgeon's practice in Tampa, Florida, and was with the University of South Florida College of Medicine.

Joanne is an active member of the Healthcare Financial Management Association and the Health Care Compliance Association. She previously served as co-chairperson of the Managed Care Education Committee for the Georgia Chapter of Healthcare Financial Management Association and is currently serving as a member of the Georgia Chapter Teams. She graduated from Georgia State University with a B.B.A. in accounting. Joanne is a Certified Healthcare Financial Professional with a specialty area in Patient Financial Services and has completed the Managed Care Certificate Program conducted by the Georgia Healthcare Financial Management Association and Mercer University.

Introduction

The U.S. health care system is becoming more complex and demanding than ever before. Each day, physicians and their office staff must deal with health insurance plans. It seems they are confronted with a perpetual game of "catch-up" and "jump-through-hoops" as they try to understand the different types of health care plans and to manage the plans' claim processing requirements.

To illustrate, consider that nearly half (46 percent) of the physicians surveyed by the Physician Payment Review Commission cited serious problems with medical billing paperwork and administrative hassles. Meanwhile, 35 percent of physicians reported that they have an inadequate understanding of Medicare billing policies and the correct use of the billing codes for visits and consultations.

Complicating the claims management process is the continued evolution of hybrid health care plans with their new rules and payment methods. During the 1980s, the health care delivery system shifted its focus from inpatient to outpatient care. During the 1990s, health insurance companies developed regional and national health care networks to contract directly with health care providers, who, in turn, must share some of the financial risk associated with the containment of health care costs. The traditional lines that once separated the physician from the hospital and from the health insurance company are blurring.

Part of the reason for changes in the health care industry is the pressure being placed on insurers and providers to control health care spending. Moreover, recent legislative initiatives at the state and federal levels have drawn attention to addressing health care and social issues such as coverage of preventive services and universal access to care. As insurance claim and reimbursement mechanisms change, physicians need to understand the changes in the insurance process so they can communicate their claims effectively and receive appropriate reimbursement. More than two thirds of the average physician's practice income comes from payments from insurance companies (third-party payers).

It is essential for physicians to understand the nature of third-party payers and to master the processing and coding of insurance claims. Healthcare Management Advisors and the American Medical Association have developed this practical guide to assist you in these tasks. This guide covers claims processing and the systems you need to set up in your office to facilitate the tracking and follow-up of claims. It also includes basic information about the coding systems used to code services, supplies, procedures, and diagnoses.

There are three reasons why you need to learn and understand this material. First, the claims filed by your practice act as a communication device to third-party payers. They communicate who was treated and why, what was done, how much was billed, and where and by whom the services were rendered. When claims are completed and filed properly, they advance the insurance reimbursement process. When claims are incomplete or filed improperly, they can be suspended for review, denied, or result in a reduced payment, all of which negatively affect your practice's income and cash flow. In fact, some studies have shown that physician practices lose between 5 percent and 30 percent of potential income because they do not manage claims effectively. No practice can afford such losses.

Second, most insurance companies have strict policies and procedures that define how claims are to be completed and filed. Payment delays and denials can result if your practice staff does not know how to properly communicate with each insurer by using its accepted format.

Third, in addition to negatively affecting payments, improperly filed claim forms can lead to increased risk of allegations of fraud or abuse. The Health Insurance Portability and Protection Act (HIPPA) of 1996 established health care fraud as a federal crime and expanded this to include all health care plans. This legislation also amended the Civil Monetary Penalty Act to apply to improper coding and patterns of medically unnecessary services. Third-party payers may suspect that practices that do not manage claims properly may also not bill properly.

A false claim is one in which any statement that is made to secure reimbursement is inaccurate. This includes, but is not limited to, claims with errors in dates, physician provider numbers, and place of service. Under HIPPA, the civil money penalties that the Office of Inspector General of the Department of Health and Human Services may assess have skyrocketed—from $2,000 to up to $10,000 per improper item on the claim form, *plus* triple the physician's original charge. The government is more concerned about patterns of behavior than individual clerical errors.

Our guide includes a glossary of insurance terminology in Appendix A. These terms are used throughout the guide, so become familiar with them before you read the chapters that follow.

1 Understanding Insurance Basics

Objectives

After completing this chapter, you should be able to:

- Explain the difference between group plans and individual insurance plans
- Understand the methods of reimbursement
- Understand the Resource Based Relative Value Scale (RBRVS) fee schedule
- Explain the difference between contracted rates and capitated rates
- Understand the processing of claims
- Understand what each modifier means and which modifier can be used for different specialties

Introduction

Health insurance has traditionally been made available to help offset the expenses of the treatment of illness or injury. Typically, a health insurance plan pays for hospital stays and some services provided by physicians. The purchaser of the health insurance (often the patient's employer) pays the insurance company a fixed amount every month, referred to as the premium. In return, the health insurance covers a defined package of medical benefits and promises to pay the bill for employees who require medical treatment. This is an example of the most common type of insurance, called indemnity insurance.

Since its inception, the system of health insurance has not changed in its basic concept. While insurance companies offer different types of health plans that vary in coverage and level of patient financial responsibility or shared payment (co-payments and deductibles), all health plans are still based on the concept of indemnity. According to *Webster's Ninth New Collegiate Dictionary*, indemnity is security; insurance; exemption from loss or damage, past or future immunity from penalty, or the punishment of past offenses; amnesty. Put more simply, an insurance policy is a contract of indemnity that provides protection to individuals against future health care costs or illnesses.

According to a recent Medical Expenditure Panel Survey (MEPS), a survey of health care utilization, expenditure, and insurance coverage data co-sponsored by the Agency for Health Care Policy and Research (AHCPR) and the National Center for Health Statistics (NCHS), approximately 83 percent of Americans have some type of health insurance. The remaining 17 percent of the population are uninsured. Additionally, government and insurance payments account for approximately 70 percent of physicians' bills and more than 90 percent of all hospital bills. This is why you need to know about the types of health insurance available and how they work. Table 1.1 illustrates the payer-mix sources of the "average physician."

Table 1.1   **Sources of Physician Payments**

Type of Health Insurance	Percentage of U.S. Population with Type of Health Insurance, 1996
Medicare	14%
Medicaid	14%
Commercial insurance	24%
HMO—managed care	12%
Other government	4%
PPO	25%
Self-pay (uninsured)	7%

Some other findings of the survey include:

- Sixty-one percent of the population had job-related coverage. Employment-based coverage represented more than 89 percent of all private insurance.

- Sixty-nine percent of people under 65 years of age were covered by private insurance. Twelve percent were covered by public insurance, and 19 percent were uninsured.

- Approximately 3 percent of the population was dually entitled to benefits from both Medicare and Medicaid.

It is important to note that the above percentages are constantly changing. Private and public insurance programs are both redesigning their products and offering more options for health care delivery. For example, both Medicare and many state Medicaid programs have designed and implemented managed care options to replace the traditional fee-for-service programs. Further, new types of programs, such as provider-sponsored organizations (PSOs), are themselves becoming insurance plans. So, in the future, the traditional separations between insurance plans and providers will continue to merge.

Types of Health Insurance Plans

There are many types of plans currently offered by insurance companies. Some of these include group insurance, individual insurance, prepaid health plans, preferred provider organizations, and point of service.

Group insurance is a plan purchased for a group of individuals (for example, employees) by an employer or other group. Group plans are offered for any member of the group, and usually their eligible dependents, under a single policy issued to the employer or the group. Personal certificates are issued to the individuals and their dependents. Equal coverage is provided for each person in the group plan.

Individual insurance is purchased by the individual on his or her own behalf. The policy is issued to the person and may also cover eligible dependents. Insuring only one individual (versus spreading the risk of insurance over a group of people) means that an individual plan usually has higher premiums and may have fewer benefits than a similar group plan.

Prepaid health plans have become more popular in the 1990s. Under a prepaid plan, physicians are reimbursed for their services at a fixed payment per person over a defined time period (for example, annually or monthly). They receive a capitated or per-person fee rather than a fee-for-service payment. The beneficiaries, called members, are limited to treatment by physicians who are employed by or under contract with the plan. Members typically pay an additional fee if they choose to see physicians who are not part of the plan (out of network). A *health maintenance organization* (HMO) is an example of a prepaid plan.

Under a *preferred provider organization* (PPO) plan, physicians who make formal arrangements with a PPO agree to provide care to individuals enrolled in the plan for predetermined, discounted fees. Individuals enroll in this type of plan because premium amounts are lower than "open" plans where the individual's choice of physician is not limited. Members who elect PPO coverage are typically limited to seeing a physician who is a member of the PPO. Patients who elect to seek services of non-PPO physicians usually must pay for the services "out-of-pocket."

Under a *point of service* (POS) plan, HMO members can decide at the point of seeking a medical service to use a nonparticipating provider (a physician or hospital that is not in the panel). When an HMO member seeks the services of a nonparticipating provider, the benefits are reduced. The member must pay out-of-pocket costs that usually amount to 20 or 30 percent of the HMO's allowable fee for the service.

Each type of insurance plan involves a contract between the covered person (or group) and the insurance plan's carrier, or originator. The health insurance contract stipulates how and to what extent physicians will be reimbursed for the services they provide to the insured persons. The third-party payer is responsible for making payments for the services, whether payment is made to the physician or to the insured person. To help you better understand the types of plans, next we will discuss the different methods of physician reimbursement.

Methods of Insurance Reimbursement

Payments to physicians for services rendered are handled in many different ways. Most commonly, the physician bills a standard fee to the patient or to the patient's insurance carrier. With the advent of HMOs, PPOs, and independent practice associations (IPAs), payments may be based on a contracted discount rate, a fee schedule, a case rate, or a capitated rate. Medicare payments are determined on the basis of a national fee schedule. Each of these payment methods is discussed next.

The Usual, Customary, and Reasonable (UCR) Method

Historically, commercial and Blue Shield plans have based physician payments on the lowest of the following:

- The physician's most frequent charge for the service
- The average charge made by physicians in the area
- The actual charge appearing on the claim for the service

This method of determining payment is called usual, customary, and reasonable (UCR). Each of the component amounts is calculated based on information submitted to the insurer. For individual physicians, a profile of all charges submitted is maintained, and the most frequent charge is identified from that information. This information is gathered for all physicians in an area. The same process is used to determine the median charges of all physicians in a geographic area. To arrive at a payment amount, the carrier compares the physician's most frequent charge (the usual), the median charge of all physicians in the area (the customary), and the actual charge submitted on the claim. Whichever amount is the lowest is used as the basis for payment (the reasonable or allowable charge).

For example, a physician usually charges $100 for a procedure, and the median charge of physicians in the area is $105. He or she submits a charge of $120 on a particular claim. For that claim, payment will be based on $100, which is the lowest of the usual ($100), customary ($105), and actual ($120) charges. **Note:** Some payers set a fee schedule that is a percentage of UCR.

Other Sources of Nondisclosed Payment Allowances

The traditional indemnity health plan is based on predefined payment allowances that may vary by physician specialty and/or geographic location. A recent survey by the Health Care Financing Administration (HCFA) revealed that more than 80 percent of indemnity insurers rely on at least one outside source of rate-setting information, such as the Health Insurance Association of America (HIAA) database or the St. Anthony's *Relative Value for Physicians* (RVP), to establish or evaluate physician payment allowances.

Relative Value Payment Schedules

Another method used by insurance plans to develop payment schedules for physician services involves the use of "relative value scales." The most well-known relative value payment schedule is the Medicare Resource Based Relative Value Scale (RBRVS). Other relative value scales include St. Anthony's *Relative Value for Physicians* (RVP) (formerly known as McGraw-Hill's *Relative Value for Physicians*), or the Florida Medical Association's Florida Relative Value Scale.

Basically, relative value scales assign a relative weight to individual services according to the basis for the scale. Some relative value scales are based on the cost of resources used and on physician effort and intensity. Some are based on a combination of both (as in the case of Medicare's RBRVS). Services that are more difficult or time consuming to perform typically have higher relative values than other services.

Payments are computed by multiplying a code's relative value by a constant dollar amount, called the conversion factor or multiplier. For example, if a procedure has a relative value of 10 and the conversion factor is $20, the fee for the service would be $200 (that is, 10 x $20). Third-party payers using relative value systems often apply additional methods, such as UCR, when determining payment limits.

Conceptually, the St. Anthony RVP and the Medicare RBRVS are similar, but they differ in their design. Following is a discussion of each of these relative value scales.

Medicare's RBRVS Payment Schedule   On January 1, 1992, Medicare began implementation of a national physician payment schedule using the RBRVS. The RBRVS was developed for the HCFA under contract by researchers at Harvard University and continues to be refined today.

Under RBRVS, a procedure's relative value unit total is the sum of three elements: the physician's work (time and intensity) (RVUWK), the practice expense related to performing the service (RVUPE), and malpractice costs associated with the service (RVUMP).

To account for economic variation across different areas of the country, the Medicare RBRVS applies a geographic component called the geographic practice cost index (GPCI). GPCIs were developed for each of the 210 Medicare payment localities. These localities were established in the early 1960s and are based on historical circumstances. The HCFA has indicated that it plans to review the current payment localities for further refinements in the future.

Medicare conversion factors (CFs) used to calculate annual payment amounts are shown in Table 1.2.

Table 1.2   **Medicare Conversion Factors, 1992-1998**

Conversion Factors	1992 CFs	1993 CFs	1994 CFs	1995 CFs	1996 CFs	1997 CFs	1998 CFs
Primary care	Not developed	Not developed	$33.718	$36.382	$35.4173	$35.7671	$36.6873
Surgical	$31.001	$31.962	$35.158	$39.447	$40.7986	$40.9603	$36.6873
Nonsurgical	$31.001	$31.249	$32.905	$34.616	$34.6293	$33.8454	$36.6873

The Medicare RBRVS payment schedule formula elements—the conversion factors, relative value units, and geographic adjustment factors—are continually reviewed for refinements. For example, Congress and the Physician Payment Review Commission (PPRC) make recommendations for the annual update of conversion factors, while the AMA/Specialty Society RVS Update Committee (RUC) and the HCFA suggest refinements in service RVUs. The RVU updates are published in an issue of the Federal Register in late October or early November and go into effect the following January 1.

The St. Anthony Relative Value for Physicians (RVP) (Formerly the McGraw-Hill RVP) In many respects, the RVP is simpler than the RBRVS. It has no geographic adjustment factors or individual RVU components to calculate. The relative value given by RVP is the number used to decide both fees and conversion factors. A drawback of the RVP is that for each major category of procedures, a separate conversion factor needs to be developed. For example, the CF developed for surgical procedures (CPT codes 10000 through 69999) cannot be used with the pathology codes (80000 through 89999).

The fee amount for the RVP is calculated using the same basic principles as those used in the RBRVS, with the exception of the location and component characteristics. For example, procedure code 99204 has an RVU of 20. If we were to take the fee for this procedure, accepted at $80, and divide it by the RVU (20), we can calculate the CF, $4 in this case. Then, to establish the fee for other procedures in this category (those from 90000 to 99999), you simply multiply the procedure-specific RVU by the CF of $4.

Use of Relative Value by Other Payers   Understanding the use and application of relative values is important not only for programs like Medicare, but also to manage reimbursements from Medicaid, Blue Cross/Blue Shield, and other commercial payers. Recent studies have shown that a significant number of insurers are currently using or are considering implementing a payment system similar to RBRVS.

In 1997, the American Medical Association (AMA) conducted a national survey of public and private payers to assess the effects of the use of RBRVS in non-Medicare health markets. The following results were obtained:

- The survey showed that 61 percent of respondents use the RBRVS in at least one product line. This compares with a 32 percent adoption rate from the 1993 Deloitte and Touche survey and a 28 percent adoption rate from a Physician Payment Review Commission (PPRC) study for its 1995 Annual Report to Congress.

- Of the 61 percent currently using the RBRVS, 65 percent have adopted and fully implemented it; 26.3 percent are undergoing implementation, meaning that phase-in or full use will begin within a year; and 3.8 percent are developing their use of the RBRVS, meaning that the decision has been made to adopt but the details have not been worked out. In addition, 17 percent of those familiar with the RBRVS are considering their potential use of it. This indicates that 78 percent of respondents who are familiar with the RBRVS are either using it or actively considering its use. Only 15 percent of those familiar with the RBRVS have considered it, but decided not to adopt, and 7 percent have not considered it at all. This can be compared to the 1993 Deloitte and Touche survey, which found that 72 percent of their respondents were using the RBRVS or actively considering its use, 32 percent had implemented it, and 40 percent were considering its use.

- Fee-for-service is the single most prominent use of the RBRVS. However, managed care is an area that has adopted the payment system to a significant degree. In fact, RBRVS is currently being used more commonly with HMOs, PPOs, POS, and managed fee-for-service.

- An area of concern with non-Medicare use of the RBRVS is the conversion factor and associated payment policies. The fear is that the RBRVS will be used solely to contain costs. This could have negative consequences for patient access.

- The adoption rate varies among four types of payers: Blue Cross/Blue Shield (BC/BS), Medicaid, workers' compensation, and other non-Medicare. A significant number, 92.5 percent, of Blue Cross/Blue Shield plans in the survey use the RBRVS, while 48.8 percent of Medicaid, 44.4 percent of workers' compensation, and 29.2 percent of other non-Medicare plans use the RBRVS.

- A large percentage of BC/BS plans use the RBRVS for fee-for-service medicine and managed care services. In fact, the largest single use of the RBRVS was for PPO plans (83.8 percent), followed by HMOs and POS plans (75.6 percent), and traditional fee-for-service plans (72.9 percent).

- The greatest use of the RBRVS was for PPOs at 64.2 percent, followed by point of service at 35.7 percent, and HMOs at 28.6 percent.

- Medicaid programs used the RBRVS mainly, 95.2 percent, for fee-for-service. They did not use the RBRVS at all for PPOs or POS and used it only minimally for HMOs and managed fee-for-service, both at 9.5 percent.

- Workers' compensation plans used the RBRVS mainly for fee-for-service, at 33.3 percent, and used it only minimally for managed care.

- Some conversion factors, which are used to define physician payment, differ significantly from Medicare's conversion factor. These findings support the findings of the PPRC study in 1994, which showed that 80 percent of managed care plans were using conversion factors in excess of Medicare's.

- BC/BS and other non-Medicare respondents had conversion factors of $44.62 and $41.16, as compared to Medicare's conversion factor of $38.68.

- Medicaid has the lowest conversion factor at $28.11.

- Workers' compensation conversion factor is at $58.22, which explains the higher rates of growth for health care costs in this area.

This survey, along with the 1993 Deloitte and Touche and 1994 PPRC studies, indicates a continuing trend toward increased non-Medicare use of the RBRVS. This recent survey by the AMA shows that all non-Medicare users of the RBRVS had a high adoption rate of Medicare payment policies, indicating a high probability for incorporating new policies. It also showed the users' willingness to adapt the RBRVS to their own needs. These results confirm the need to maintain the RBRVS as an accurate, comprehensive standard, uniformly containing all medical services nationwide.

Contracted Rates With HMOs, PPOs, IPAs, and PSOs

An increasingly popular reimbursement method involves a contract between the physician and another entity (such as an HMO, a PPO, an IPA, or a PSO) for reduced fees in exchange for patient volume. The physician may agree to provide services at a discount of the normal fee with the understanding that the HMO, PPO, IPA, or PSO will refer patients to the physician or provide the physician with a pool of existing patients.

Capitated Rates

The newest type of managed care payments is a fixed payment amount per patient per month from an HMO, PPO, or IPA. This is called a capitation arrangement. Under a capitation plan, the physician provides the full range of normal services to patients enrolled and covered under the capitation health plan benefits but does not bill on a fee-for-service basis.

In some ways, capitation is similar to a "retainer" fee, in that the provider is paid a fixed amount on a periodic basis to prepare and allocate care to patients when they need care.

Capitated contracts are almost always negotiable. These health plans contract with select physicians, primarily primary health care physicians (FPs, GPs, Internal Medicine, etc) to manage the health care needs of the patient for whom they have a policy. The physician is paid a fixed amount each month for patients who selected him or her as their primary physician. For example, if a health plan had 300 patients who selected Dr. Smith as their primary physician, and the plan agreed to pay Dr. Smith $12 per patient per month (PPPM or PMPM [per member per month]), Dr. Smith would be paid $3,600 each month regardless of the number of patients seen or treatments provided. While guaranteed a fixed payment amount every month, Dr. Smith assumes the risk that the cost of providing care may exceed the payment amount, for which he would not receive additional reimbursement. The positive aspects of a capitation arrangement are a guaranteed fixed payment, no bad debt, and an assured cash flow. In some plans there still may be patient responsibilities of deductibles, co-insurance, and co-payments. These are very infrequent. Some covered patients may require little or no services, but others may require extensive services.

To succeed under capitation, physicians must learn to control costs through controlled service utilization, emphasis on preventive health care service, and the use of cost-effective tests, supplies, and allied health personnel such as nurse practitioners (NPs) and physician assistants (PAs). Primary care providers are encouraged not to overutilize ancillaries (x-ray and lab) or high-cost procedures that have limited positive clinical outcomes. Accounting mechanisms are essential. Many practices get into difficulty with IBNR (incurred but not received). They have authorized a test or procedure that is not billed or accomplished in the capitation period. The accounting at the end of the period may show a false profit if the IBNR is not factored in.

A practice should perform a cost-accounting analysis by procedure code to identify the practices' costs per service and per unit. This can only be done using RBRVS to calculate cost, profit, and loss. The data obtained can be used to provide some negotiating leverage at the bargaining table.

The capitation rate per patient is normally established by the insurer, after consideration is given to the number and type of services likely to be provided to patients covered by the plan. Physicians must thoroughly research the contract and the financial agreements. Many have signed up for capitated plans without modeling the capitated arrangement based on current characteristics of their physician practice and are now paying for their lack of research in providing capitated services. The two most important questions are "How much do I get?" and "What am I required by contract to provide for the payment?"

How Claims Are Processed by Insurance Carriers

Although each third-party payer has its own procedures and systems for processing claims, most payers perform similar functions from the time they receive a claim until they pay or deny it. The following sections explain these functions.

Physician claims are usually sent to insurance plans two ways—printed on paper claims that are mailed or faxed to the plan, or sent electronically via modem after the data is stored on computer media such as diskettes, tapes, or CD-ROMs.

Processing of Paper Claims

Many physicians submit paper claims to third-party payers. The most common method of reporting claims is the use of the universal claim form (HCFA-1500). A sample of the HCFA-1500 is shown in Exhibit 1.1. Some health plans still accept a physician's charge ticket (often termed a superbill or encounter form) to report services rendered. Note that the claim form should provide areas for the information needed to report physician services for payment—payer, patient, physician, and place-of-service information—as well as for diagnostic codes, procedure codes, and fees.

Contrast the HCFA-1500 to the sample encounter form shown in Exhibit 1.2. Each practice creates its own encounter form and lists information and codes relevant to the practice's needs. These forms are often designed with the assistance of a consultant familiar with payer requirements and coding issues, or with the help of a trained printer representative. A poorly designed encounter form can adversely affect your practice's third-party payments. They should be updated annually to reflect the new CPT coding changes.

Medicare will not accept encounter forms or charge tickets. When submitting paper claims to Medicare, you must use the HCFA-1500 form. HCFA discourages the use of paper claims and prefers electronic claims. As a disincentive to use of paper claims, they may impose a monetary penalty or delay the processing of paper claims over electronic claims. In addition to Medicare, virtually all third-party payers accept the HCFA-1500 form. To review how to complete a HCFA-1500 form, see Chapter 5.

Processing a paper claim involves the following steps:

1. Paper claims are received through the mail and microfilmed or microfiched by the payer. Any attachments accompanying claims are separated for microfilming. Since the person at the payer who handles this function may film thousands of claims each day, he or she may not be able to match the attachments to their associated claims if the following information is not provided on the attachments:

   Physician name

   Physician identification number

   Patient name

   Patient policy number

   Date of the service

Failure to include the above information on attachments may result in claim delays, requests for additional information from the payer, or, in some cases, claim denials.

2. After your claim has been microfilmed, it may go directly to the claims processing department. In some cases the claim may be screened. Screeners review basic claims data to verify:

   a. Eligibility

   b. That the patient's policy is in effect

   c. That the services provided are covered by the patient's contract

Exhibit 1.1   Sample HCFA-1500 Form

PLEASE DO NOT STAPLE IN THIS AREA

← CARRIER →

☐☐ PICA

HEALTH INSURANCE CLAIM FORM

PICA ☐☐

1. MEDICARE	MEDICAID	CHAMPUS	CHAMPVA	GROUP HEALTH PLAN	FECA BLK LUNG	OTHER	1a. INSURED'S I.D. NUMBER (FOR PROGRAM IN ITEM 1)
☐ (Medicare #)	☐ (Medicaid #)	☐ (Sponsor's SSN)	☐ (VA File #)	☐ (SSN or ID)	☐ (SSN)	☐ (ID)	

2. PATIENT'S NAME (Last Name, First Name, Middle Initial)

3. PATIENT'S BIRTH DATE MM | DD | YY   SEX   M ☐   F ☐

4. INSURED'S NAME (Last Name, First Name, Middle Initial)

5. PATIENT'S ADDRESS (No., Street)

6. PATIENT RELATIONSHIP TO INSURED
Self ☐   Spouse ☐   Child ☐   Other ☐

7. INSURED'S ADDRESS (No., Street)

CITY   STATE

8. PATIENT STATUS
Single ☐   Married ☐   Other ☐

CITY   STATE

ZIP CODE   TELEPHONE (Include Area Code) ( )

Employed ☐   Full-Time Student ☐   Part-Time Student ☐

ZIP CODE   TELEPHONE (INCLUDE AREA CODE) ( )

9. OTHER INSURED'S NAME (Last Name, First Name, Middle Initial)

10. IS PATIENT'S CONDITION RELATED TO:

11. INSURED'S POLICY GROUP OR FECA NUMBER

a. OTHER INSURED'S POLICY OR GROUP NUMBER

a. EMPLOYMENT? (CURRENT OR PREVIOUS)
☐ YES   ☐ NO

a. INSURED'S DATE OF BIRTH MM | DD | YY   SEX   M ☐   F ☐

b. OTHER INSURED'S DATE OF BIRTH MM | DD | YY   SEX   M ☐   F ☐

b. AUTO ACCIDENT?   PLACE (State)
☐ YES   ☐ NO

b. EMPLOYER'S NAME OR SCHOOL NAME

c. EMPLOYER'S NAME OR SCHOOL NAME

c. OTHER ACCIDENT?
☐ YES   ☐ NO

c. INSURANCE PLAN NAME OR PROGRAM NAME

d. INSURANCE PLAN NAME OR PROGRAM NAME

10d. RESERVED FOR LOCAL USE

d. IS THERE ANOTHER HEALTH BENEFIT PLAN?
☐ YES   ☐ NO   *If yes*, return to and complete item 9 a-d.

READ BACK OF FORM BEFORE COMPLETING & SIGNING THIS FORM.
12. PATIENT'S OR AUTHORIZED PERSON'S SIGNATURE I authorize the release of any medical or other information necessary to process this claim. I also request payment of government benefits either to myself or to the party who accepts assignment below.

SIGNED _____ DATE _____

13. INSURED'S OR AUTHORIZED PERSON'S SIGNATURE I authorize payment of medical benefits to the undersigned physician or supplier for services described below.

SIGNED _____

← PATIENT AND INSURED INFORMATION →

14. DATE OF CURRENT: ◄ ILLNESS (First symptom) OR INJURY (Accident) OR PREGNANCY(LMP)   MM | DD | YY

15. IF PATIENT HAS HAD SAME OR SIMILAR ILLNESS. GIVE FIRST DATE MM | DD | YY

16. DATES PATIENT UNABLE TO WORK IN CURRENT OCCUPATION
FROM MM | DD | YY   TO MM | DD | YY

17. NAME OF REFERRING PHYSICIAN OR OTHER SOURCE

17a. I.D. NUMBER OF REFERRING PHYSICIAN

18. HOSPITALIZATION DATES RELATED TO CURRENT SERVICES
FROM MM | DD | YY   TO MM | DD | YY

19. RESERVED FOR LOCAL USE

20. OUTSIDE LAB?   ☐ YES   ☐ NO $ CHARGES

21. DIAGNOSIS OR NATURE OF ILLNESS OR INJURY. (RELATE ITEMS 1,2,3 OR 4 TO ITEM 24E BY LINE)
1. └___.___   3. └___.___
2. └___.___   4. └___.___

22. MEDICAID RESUBMISSION CODE   ORIGINAL REF. NO.

23. PRIOR AUTHORIZATION NUMBER

24. A DATE(S) OF SERVICE From MM DD YY To MM DD YY	B Place of Service	C Type of Service	D PROCEDURES, SERVICES, OR SUPPLIES (Explain Unusual Circumstances) CPT/HCPCS	MODIFIER	E DIAGNOSIS CODE	F $ CHARGES	G DAYS OR UNITS	H EPSDT Family Plan	I EMG	J COB	K RESERVED FOR LOCAL USE
1											
2											
3											
4											
5											
6											

25. FEDERAL TAX I.D. NUMBER   SSN ☐ EIN ☐

26. PATIENT'S ACCOUNT NO.

27. ACCEPT ASSIGNMENT? (For govt. claims, see back)
☐ YES   ☐ NO

28. TOTAL CHARGE $

29. AMOUNT PAID $

30. BALANCE DUE $

31. SIGNATURE OF PHYSICIAN OR SUPPLIER INCLUDING DEGREES OR CREDENTIALS (I certify that the statements on the reverse apply to this bill and are made a part thereof.)

SIGNED _____ DATE _____

32. NAME AND ADDRESS OF FACILITY WHERE SERVICES WERE RENDERED (If other than home or office)

33. PHYSICIAN'S, SUPPLIER'S BILLING NAME, ADDRESS, ZIP CODE & PHONE #

PIN#   GRP#

← PHYSICIAN OR SUPPLIER INFORMATION →

(APPROVED BY AMA COUNCIL ON MEDICAL SERVICE 8/88)

PLEASE PRINT OR TYPE

APPROVED OMB-0938-0008 FORM HCFA-1500 (12-90),   FORM RRB-1500,
APPROVED OMB-1215-0055 FORM OWCP-1500,   APPROVED OMB-0720-0001 (CHAMPUS)

Exhibit 1.2   Sample Encounter Form (Superbill)

STATE LIC. # 123456789
SOC. SEC. # 000-11-0000
PIN # _____

JOHN R. JOHNSON, M.D.
Family Practice
1000 MAIN STREET, SOME PLACE, USA 70000

TELEPHONE: (123) 234-5678

☐ PRIVATE   ☐ BLUECROSS   ☐ IND.   ☐ MEDICARE   ☐ MEDI-CAL   ☐ HMO   ☐ PPO

PATIENT'S LAST NAME	FIRST	ACCOUNT #	BIRTHDATE / /	SEX ☐ MALE ☐ FEMALE	TODAY'S DATE / /
INSURANCE COMPANY	SUBSCRIBER		PLAN #	SUB. #	GROUP

ASSIGNMENT: I hereby assign my insurance benefits to be paid directly to the undersigned physician. I am financially responsible for non-covered services.
SIGNED: (Patient, or Parent, if Minor)   DATE: /   /

RELEASE: I hereby authorize the physician to release to my insurance carrers any information required to process this claim.
SIGNED: (Patient, or Parent, if Minor)   DATE: /   /

✔	DESCRIPTION	M/Care	CPT/Mod	DxRe	FEE	✔	DESCRIPTION	M/Care	CPT/Mod	DxRe	FEE	✔	DESCRIPTION	M/Care	CPT/Mod	DxRe	FEE
	OFFICE CARE						PROCEDURES						INJECTIONS/IMMUNIZATIONS				
	NEW PATIENT						Treadmill (In Office)		93015				Tetanus Toxoid		90703		
	Focused		99201				24 Hr. Holter Monitor		93224				Hypertet	J1670	90782		
	Expanded		99202				Recording Only		93225				Pneumococcal		90732		
	Detailed		99203				Interp. & Report		93227				Influenza		90724		
	Comprehensive-Mod.		99204				EKG w/Interpretation		93000				TB Skin Test (PPD)		86585		
	Comprehensive-High		99205				EKG (Medicare)		93005				Antigen Injection-Single		95115		
							Sigmoidoscopy		45300				Multiple		95117		
	ESTABLISHED PATIENT						Sigmoidoscopy, Flexible		45330				B12 Injection	J3420	90782		
	Minimal		99211				Sigmoidos. , Flex. w/Bx.		45331				Injection, IM		90788		
	Focused		99212				Spirometry, FEV/FVC		94010				Compazine	J0780	90782		
	Expanded		99213				Spirometry, Post-Dilator		94060				Demerol	J2175	90782		
	Detailed		99214										Vistaril	J3410	90782		
	Comprehensive-Mod.		99215										Susphrine	J0170	90782		
	Comprehensive-High		99215				LABORATORY						Decadron	J0890	90782		
							Routine Venipuncture		36415				Estradiol	J1000	90782		
	CONSULTATION-OFFICE						Urinalysis, Chemical		81005				Testosterone	J1080	90782		
	Focused		99241				Throat Culture		87081				Lidocaine	J2000	90782		
	Expanded		99242				Occult Blood		82270				Solumedrol	J2920	90782		
	Detailed		99243				Pap Handling Charge		99000				Solucortef	J1720	90782		
	Comprehensive-Mod.		99244				Pap Life Guard		88150-90				Hydeltra	J1690	90782		
	Comprehensive-High		99245				Gram Stain		87205				Pen Procaine	J2510	90788		
	Dr.						Wet Mount		87210								
	Post-op Exam		99024				Urine Drug Screen		99000				INJECTIONS - JOINT/BURSA				
	EVALUATION/CASE MANAGEMENT												Arthrocentesis-Small Jt.		20600		
	Brief Eval.-30 Mins.		99361										Arthrocent.-Interm. Jts.		20605		
	Intermed. Eval.-60 Mins.		99362				SUPPLIES						Arthrocent.-Major Jts.		20610		
	Telephone-Brief		99371										Trigger Point Injection		20550		
	Telephone-Intermed.		99372										MISCELLANEOUS				
	Telephone-Complex		99373														

DIAGNOSIS:

	ICD-9											
Abdominal Pain	789.0_	Gout	274.0	C.V.A. - Acute	436.	Electrolyte Dis.	276.9	Herpes Simplex	054.9
Abscess (Site)	682.9	Asthma	493.90	Cere. Vas. Accid. (Old)	438	Fatigue	780.7	Herpes Zoster	053.9
Adverse Drug Rx	995.2	Asthmatic Bronchitis	491.20	Cerumen	380.4	Fibrocys. Br. Dis	610.1	Hydrocele	603.9
Alcohol Detox	291.8	Atrial Fib.	427.31	Chestwall Pain	786.59	Fracture (Site)	829.0	Hyperlipidemia	272.4
Alcoholism	303.90	Atrial Tachycardia	427.89	Cholecystitis	575.0	Open/Close		Hypertension	401.9
Allergic Rhinitis	477.9	Bowel Obstruct.	560.9	Cholelithiasis	574.00	Fungal Infect. (Site)	117.9	Hyperthyroidism	242.9
Allergy	995.3	Breast Mass	611.72	COPD	496	Gastric Ulcer	531.90	Hypothyroidism	244.9
Alzheimer's Dis.	290.1_	Bronchitis, Acute	466.0	Cirrhosis	571.5	Gastritis	535.0	Labyrinthitis	386.30
Anemia	285.9	Bursitis	727.3	Cong. Heart Fail.	428.9	Gastroenteritis	558.9	Lipoma (Site)	214.9
Anemia - Pernicious	281.0	Cancer, Breast (Site)	174.9	Conjunctivitis	372.30	G.I. Bleeding	578.9	Lymphoma	202.8
Angina	413.9	Metastatic (Site)	198.2	Contusion (Site)	924.9	Glomerulonephritis	583.89	Mit. Valve Prolapse	424.0
Anxiety Synd.	300.00	Colon	153.9	Costochondritis	733.99	Headache	784.0	Myocard. Infarction (Area)	410.9
Appendicitis	541	Cancer, Rectal	154.1	Depression	311.	Headache, Tension	307.81	M.I., Old	412
Arterioscl. H.D.	414.0_	Lung (Site)	162.9	Dermatitis	692.9	Migraine (Type)	346.9	Myositis	729.1
Arthritis, Osteo.	715.90	Skin (Site)	173.9	Diabetes Mellitus	250.00	Hemorrhoids	455.6	Nausea/Vomiting	787.01
Rheumatoid	714.0	Card. Arrhythmia (Type)	427.9	Diabetic Ketosis	250.10	Hernia, Hiatal	553.3	Neuralgia	729.2
Arthritis, Osteo.		Cardiomyopathy	425.4	Diverticulitis	562.11	Inguinal	550.9	Nevus (Site)	216.9
Lupus	710.0	Cellulitis (Site)	682.9	Diverticulosis	562.10	Hepatitis	573.3	Obesity	278.00

DIAGNOSIS: (IF NOT CHECKED ABOVE)

SERVICES PERFORMED AT: ☐ Office   ☐ E.R.   ☐   ☐ CLAIM CONTAINS NO ORDERED REFERRING SERVICE

REFERRING PHYSICIAN & I.D. NUMBER

RETURN APPOINTMENT INFORMATION:
5 - 10 - 15 - 20 - 30 - 40 - 60

[DAYS] [WKS.] [MOS.] [PRN]

NEXT APPOINTMENT
M - T - W - TH - F - S
DATE /   /   TIME:

AM
PM

ACCEPT ASSIGNMENT?
☐ YES
☐ NO

DOCTOR'S SIGNATURE

INSTRUCTIONS TO PATIENT FOR FILING INSURANCE CLAIMS:

1. Complete upper portion of this form, sign and date.
2. Attach this form to your own insurance company's form for direct reimbursement.

**MEDICARE PATIENTS - DO NOT SEND THIS TO MEDICARE.
WE WILL SUBMIT THE CLAIM FOR YOU.**

☐ CASH
☐ CHECK   #
☐ VISA
☐ MC
☐ CO-PAY

TOTAL TODAY'S FEE	
OLD BALANCE	
TOTAL DUE	
AMOUNT REC'D. TODAY	

    d. That any required preoperative clearances were obtained

    e. Any other information

Increasingly, the screening functions are being handled by computers at the time the claim is entered.

3. Claims processors enter the information on your claim into the payer's computer system. Because of the vast number of claims the payer must process each day, your claim will spend only two or three minutes with the processor. If the information your practice has provided is incomplete or illegible, the claim may be delayed, suspended for manual review, or denied. Paper claims have a significantly higher data error entry rate than electronic claims.

If your claim includes support documentation that provides information about unusual circumstances, the claim may be forwarded from the processor to a supervisor. The supervisor either makes a payment decision or gives the claim to the payer's medical review staff.

Some payers utilize optical scanners to process HCFA-1500 forms. The scanners digitize the data on the claim form into their claims processing system for adjudication.

Because claims processors and their immediate supervisors have limited training in medicine, they may not understand operative reports and other support documentation. When you submit additional documentation to explain or justify your services, include a brief cover letter that gives a simple description of what was done, why it was done, and the unusual circumstances that affected the performance of the procedure or service.

Common Problems of "Clean" Paper Claim Processing

Many claim delays and denials result from improper, incomplete, or inaccurate information on claims. These are sometimes called "dirty claims." The following types of problems are often the cause of dirty claims:

1. Illegible handwriting

2. Lack of physician name, identification, or signature

3. Lack of patient name or policy number (name submitted for Medicare must be identical to the printing on the Medicare card, including middle initials)

4. Out-of-date patient information

5. Outdated codes (CPT, HCPCS, and ICD-9-CM)

6. Improper place-of-service code

7. Lack of referring physician name or identification (when appropriate).

8. Illogical relationships between services and patient diagnoses

9. Service that does not match Medicare utilization screening criteria

Many practice management computer systems and electronic claims submission programs encourage you to submit cleaner claims by requiring that basic claim information be included. It should be a policy in your practice to ensure that the claims you submit have complete, correct, and current information.

Processing of Electronic Claims

An alternative to submitting paper claims by mail is to submit them electronically to the payer either directly or through a claims clearinghouse. The electronic process usually requires that you have a computer, a modem, and special software. Firms offer simple terminals or data entry devices specifically for the purpose of submitting claims. Most physician practice management computer systems provide capabilities for you to submit claims electronically. Computer vendors, BC/BS, and other organizations can provide you with information about setting up an electronic claims submission system. Some Medicare carriers provide free software.

Electronic claims submission (ECS) has several advantages over paper claims. On average, ECS claims are paid more quickly than paper claims. Medicare, for example, is mandated to pay ECS claims within 14 days, while the paper claim threshold is 27 days.

Most ECS software contains claim-editing features that detect and report incomplete claims, invalid codes, or other problems that will cause the claim to be rejected before it is sent. These are basic edits such as a prostatectomy in a female or a Pap smear in a male. This edit feature forces the practice to file clean claims.

Most practices have found that ECS is about one-third less expensive than processing paper claims. Third-party payers also enjoy cost savings through the receipt of electronic claims. Because of the stringent ECS requirements and edits at claims clearinghouses that force users to create cleaner claims, ECS claims are less likely to be rejected by payers. Payment posting and reconciliation of claims are far superior with the use of ECS. There is also a tape-to-tape rollover (Medicare to Medicaid, etc.) that cannot be done with paper claims.

Finally, electronic claims are easier to submit than are paper claims, they are much more likely to be paid, and they are transmitted quickly from your computer to the payer's computer.

Drawbacks of ECS include the following:

- For claims that require support documentation, you may need to mail the documentation to the payer.

- There are startup expenses associated with generating ECS claims if your practice is not automated.

The first drawback should be eliminated as ECS systems begin to accommodate the electronic transmission of reports, radiographs, and related information. As systems progress, claims may be generated in the future from an electronic medical record, which will enhance proper documentation.

There are several methods of submitting claims electronically. You can:

- Obtain a computer and software that allow you to submit claims directly to major third-party payers, such as Medicare and Blue Shield.

- Submit your claims electronically to a clearinghouse that in turn routes the claims electronically to various third-party payers.

- Give your paper claims to a service bureau that enters the claims and submits them electronically on behalf of your practice.

- Use a combination of submitting directly to major payers (such as Medicare) and through claims clearinghouses for other payers.

Because not all third-party payers accept electronic claims, even the most automated practices, clearinghouses, and service bureaus must still produce and mail a large number of paper claims. In most systems a paper claim is produced from the electronically stored data. Thus, retyping the claim is unnecessary.

This chapter discussed how claims are processed. The next chapter describes the types of plans offered by third-party payers, including Blue Cross/Blue Shield, Medicare, Medicaid, workers' compensation, CHAMPUS, and CHAMPVA.

2 Types of Insurance and Third-Party Payers

Objectives

After completing this chapter, you should be able to:

- Understand the purpose of commercial carriers

- Understand the differences that distinguish Blue Cross and Blue Shield plans from other commercial insurance carriers

- Identify the different types of Blue Cross/Blue Shield accounts

- Describe the difference between Medicare and Medicaid

- Understand the four most common policies under Medicare and their effect on reimbursement

- Explain the purpose of the Civilian Health and Medical Program of the Veterans Affairs (CHAMPVA)

- Explain the purpose of the Civilian Health and Medical Program of the Uniformed Services (CHAMPUS)

- Explain the independent practice association (IPA) plan

- Describe the difference between health maintenance organizations (HMOs) and preferred provider organizations (PPOs)

- Explain the provider-sponsored organizations (PSOs)

- Discuss what workers' compensation insurance covers and explain which federal and state agencies administer the programs

Introduction

In the United States, there are more than 3,000 organizations that may be classified as third-party payers, each offering a variety of health care benefit packages. They range from small corporate self-funded plans to Medicare. This chapter describes the different types of third-party payers, both public and private.

Commercial Carriers

Background Information

Commercial carriers are private, for-profit organizations that sell health insurance policies to groups (usually employers) and/or individuals. In return for premiums paid by employers or employees, they determine a defined set of health benefits, which may vary on a company-by-company or individual-by-individual basis. Major insurance companies such as Aetna, Cigna, Prudential, and Travelers are examples of commercial carriers.

Commercial insurance companies operate in the private sector and offer a number of different health insurance benefit plans to serve the needs of employers, business, and government. Generally, physicians do not have special contract agreements with commercial carriers, so the patient bears the ultimate responsibility for the bill and the filing of the claim. Some providers may want to file for the patient to ensure a clean, timely claim. Most providers do not require payment if the patient is "insured." Therefore, the risk of an "aged claim" falls on the provider.

The term *commercial insurance* has historically been used to refer to traditional indemnity health plans that reimburse fee-for-service, generally based on an 80/20 split, with the insurance covering 80 percent of the health plan allowance and the patient being responsible for the remaining 20 percent co-insurance. Most commercial insurance plans have predefined patient deductibles and co-insurance provisions. The physician's office staff is responsible for contacting the plan to determine the patient's deductible and co-insurance status before rendering services.

Commercial Insurance "Nondisclosed" Payment Allowance

The traditional indemnity plan is based on predefined payment allowances that may vary by physician specialty and/or geographic location. Results of a recent survey show that 80 percent of indemnity insurers rely on at least one outside source of information, such as the HIAA or the St. Anthony RVP, to establish or evaluate their physician payment allowances.

Most commercial health plans do not release a fee schedule to physicians as the Medicare and workers' compensation programs do, so physicians do not usually know what they will be paid before billing the claim. Physicians should pay close attention to commercial payment explanation of benefit (EOB) reports to see how close payments are to charges. This comparison will be helpful for future charge adjustments. It is important that billing for any service is the same for all carriers. Medicare does not allow different billing for their services from those of commercial payers. The allowed payments may differ, but the amount billed may not. Physicians should also remember that not all services they render may be covered by all insurance plans. Coverage for health services are defined in the patient's health insurance policy, which is based on a contract between the insurance company and the patient or employer. Therefore, each insurance company health plan offers different levels of medical and financial coverage. Verification of insurance coverage is very important.

Coordination of Benefits

The majority of commercial insurance health plans have coordination of benefits (COB) clauses that help to define primary and secondary payer status for a pending claim. Many plans also utilize the "gender rule" or the "birthday rule" to assign primary responsibility. Under the gender rule, the male of the household is first in line. Under the birthday rule, the plan of the parent whose birthday falls earlier in the year is primary to the plan of the parent whose birthday falls later in the year, referring to the month and day. If both parents have the same birthday, then the plan that has covered a parent the longest is primary.

Relationship to Other Health Insurance Programs

- **Medicare**. Commercial insurance is almost always primary to any public program, including Medicare. Certain exceptions are provided in the Medicare Secondary Payer rules.

- **Medicaid**. If a person is eligible for Medicaid as well as commercial insurance benefits, commercial insurance always pays first.

- **CHAMPUS**. When a beneficiary is covered under another medical insurance plan, CHAMPUS is always secondary, except for Medicaid, the Indian Health Service, or any plan that is specifically designated as a CHAMPUS supplement.

- **Workers' compensation**. Expenses for medical care related to job-connected illness or injury are paid by the workers' compensation program. Only when benefits are exhausted under the workers' compensation program does commercial insurance assume responsibility for the balance.

- **Private automobile insurance**. Any amounts paid by commercial insurance resulting from an automobile accident when the claims are also payable under a policy of automobile insurance may be subject to recovery under the Federal Claims Collections Act.

Claim Submission

It is the responsibility of physicians to accurately report the level or type of service they provide to patients according to the coding guidelines and reimbursement rules of the AMA and HCFA. Through accurate coding, the health plan's claim adjudication division will attempt to process the physician's claim and the physician will receive appropriate reimbursement.

Most commercial insurance companies are required to accept the HCFA-1500 for claims processing. Most commercial insurance companies have claim "deadlines" or a set time limit for which the claim is processable. The period usually starts on the date of the physician service and may continue for three months, six months, or a year, depending on their policy. So it is important that claims for patients with commercial insurance be mailed within four to six days after the date of service. A claim filed on time but not settled expediently because of administrative delays should still be paid, even if the processing time extends beyond the filing date. Proof of filing may be necessary, as well as evidence that the claim continues to be actively pursued. Failure to meet this objective may indicate serious billing problems.

Blue Cross/Blue Shield Plans

Blue Cross/Blue Shield (BC/BS) plans are a federation of individual nonprofit community corporations that contract with physicians, hospitals, and various other health entities to provide services to their insured companies and individuals. BC/BS refers to the persons they insure as subscribers, not policyholders, and they are issued a certificate, not a policy. The certificate defines the health-care benefits and obligations of the medical plan. The word *plan* refers to each separately incorporated, locally administered corporation authorized to use the BC/BS name and symbol.

Currently, there are eight Blue Cross plans and 10 Blue Shield plans, which are part of the 55 Blue Cross and Blue Shield plans in the United States and Puerto Rico. Blue Cross primarily covers hospital services, outpatient care, some institutional services, and home care. By contrast, Blue Shield typically covers physician services and, in some cases, dental, outpatient, and vision care.

Collectively, Blue Cross and Blue Shield Member Plans provide health care coverage for more than 68.7 million people in the 50 states, the District of Columbia, and Puerto Rico. In the United States, more than 80 percent of hospitals and nearly 70 percent of physicians contract directly with Blue Cross and Blue Shield Member Plans. Collectively, Blue Cross and Blue Shield Member Plans make up the nation's largest provider of managed care services. More than

41.3 million people—roughly one in seven Americans—are enrolled in a Blue Cross and Blue Shield managed care plan.

The plans are organized locally, and, in some states, both Blue Cross and Blue Shield share offices. In other states, they are entirely separate organizations. Activities of Blue Cross and Blue Shield plans are coordinated nationally by the Blue Cross and Blue Shield Association of America. The national organization coordinates services and benefits among different BC/BS plans for those with offices in multiple states, as well as providing other related services.

BC/BS plans differ from commercial carrier plans in that they can operate as nonprofit corporations and write contracts directly with providers. If nonprofit, the BC/BS plan must obtain approval from its state insurance department before raising rates or changing coverage. Most BC/BS plans offer health maintenance organizations (HMOs), preferred provider organizations (PPOs), and point-of-service (POS) plans in addition to group and individual fee-for-service plans.

Physician reimbursement under Blue Shield plans is based on the usual, customary, and reasonable (UCR) payment method. Under UCR, the allowable is the lower of the physician's charge for a service or the UCR amount, or the "average" charge for the service by other physicians in the community who provide the same services. More plans are using the RBRVS to define payment schedules, while other plans use a fixed rate per patient, called capitation. Blue Shield plans, like other commercial insurance plans, will continue to shift their reimbursement methods away from UCR to RBRVS and capitated methods.

Types of Accounts

The majority of BC/BS business can be classified into the following types of accounts:

1. Local or regular business

2. Central certification

3. Federal Employee Program (FEP)

4. NASCO accounts

The following sections describe each type of account and provide procedures for filing claims.

Local or Regular Business Accounts   Local accounts are those in which plan members are located within the geographic territory of the plan. BC/BS issues identification cards locally, and all identification contract numbers will be preceded by the local plan's three-letter prefix.

When a patient presents a local or regular business ID card, transmit the following information from the card to the claim form.

1. Subscriber's name

2. Subscriber's contract number, alpha prefix, and other suffixes

3. Subscriber's group number

4. BC/BS plan code

This is just one example of information provided on the back of a Blue Cross card. Be sure to review the back of each card. Instructions may differ among the various Blue Cross groups. A copy of a sample ID card is shown below (Exhibit 2.1).

Exhibit 2.1   **Sample BlueCross/BlueShield ID Card**

Central Certification   Central certification is a national account system used to administer benefits for employees of companies that have plants, offices, and people in several different states; for employees who travel or change location frequently; and for firms that have all personnel, payroll, and health coverage records in one place.

All records are kept by one plan, called the Control Plan, which is usually the plan located in the company's headquarters city. The Control Plan issues identification cards to all employees of the company, regardless of their location.

A central certification subscriber is treated the same as a subscriber of a local Blue Cross plan. Members deal with their local Blue Cross and Blue Shield plan initially. Physicians are paid by the local Blue Cross and Blue Shield plan on receipt of an approval from the Control Plan.

The top right of the Blue Cross and Blue Shield central certification card has a map of the United States within which are the words "central certification"; directly below the map is the subscriber's effective date. The bottom of the card gives the following information in this order:

The subscriber's name: John Q. Public

Identification code and number: XYZ123-45-6789

Group number: XYZ111

(This is usually a special six-character group number. The three letters identify the company and the subscriber's work form; the three numbers identify the Blue Cross and Blue Shield control plan.)

Blue Shield plan code: 222

(Blue Shield plan code booklets are available for identifying the name of the plan.)

Blue Cross plan code: 111

(Blue Cross plan code booklets are available for identifying the name of the plan.)

Group name: XYZ Corporation

Federal Employee Program (FEP)   The Blue Cross and Blue Shield Association, on behalf of all Blue Cross and Blue Shield plans, contracts with the U.S. Office of Personnel Management (OPM) to provide government-wide service benefit plan coverage to 5 million federal employees and dependents, called the Federal Employee Program (FEP). Each year the benefits and premiums are renegotiated with OPM. Benefits and rates for Blue Cross and Blue Shield employees are the same nationwide.

The FEP identification card is a nationally recognized card with the words *Government-Wide Service Benefit Plan* across the top. The card aids in admissions to hospitals without having to check with the patient's employer or make other financial arrangements. All claims are processed through the local plan's office. There is a toll-free customer service number that all customers may use for the claims filing procedures, requests for additional claim forms for patients, and benefits information. A sample of the FEP ID card is shown below (Exhibit 2.2).

Exhibit 2.2   **Sample Federal Employee Program ID Card**

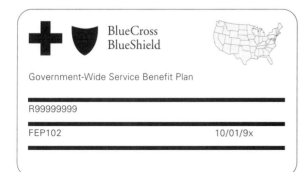

TO THE HOSPITAL OR DOCTOR
Please notify your local Blue Cross or Blue Shield Plan on its regular claim form when services are provided.
TO THE FEDERAL EMPLOYEE OR ANNUITANT
1. The Government-Wide Service Benefit Plan Brochure (BRI 41-25) provides information regarding benefits of the Program and how they may be obtained.
2. Whenever you inquire about your coverage, please contact the Blue Cross or Blue Shield office serving the area where you live or work, or Blue Cross and Blue Shield Federal Employee Program,. 550 12th Street, S.W., Washington, D.C. 20024. Always give your identification number and the enrollment code which appear on the face of this card.
3. Coverage normally ceases for children who marry or attain the age of 22 years. To continue protection, they should apply promptly to their local Blue Cross and Blue Shield Plan for a conversion contract.

ENROLLMENT CODES		
	HIGH OPTION	LOW OPTION
SELF ONLY	101	104
FAMILY	102	105

Employees may select from various options. The following list of coverage classification codes is used to identify the type of benefit option:

Enrollment Information—Classification Codes

101   Self Only/High Option

102   Self and Family/High Option

104   Self Only/Standard Option

105   Self and Family/Standard Option

All FEP ID cards for federal employees are issued by the FEP Operations Center in Washington, DC. Employees can get replacement cards by writing to:

Blue Cross and Blue Shield Federal Employee Program
550 12th St. S.W.
Washington, DC 20065
Attention: FEP Source Records Department

NASCO Accounts   NASCO (National Account Service Company Operations) is an automated claim processing system for any national account that contracts to be a part of the system. One of the advantages of this system is the consistent way in which contract benefits are processed and paid nationwide. Several plans throughout the country utilize the NASCO system. For example, three automotive programs—Chrysler, Ford Motor Company, and General Motors—provide health care benefits through the Blue Shield network.

Chrysler Program. Chrysler is a self-insured program underwritten by Blue Shield. Because Chrysler participates in the central certification program for outpatient and inpatient benefits in most states, all claims should be billed to the Blue Shield carrier for the state in which services were rendered to the program member or eligible dependent. This means that physicians who participate must file the patient's insurance, take assignment, and abide by the plan's UCR payment allowance as payment in full.

This program operates under intense utilization review for all hospital admissions and treatment with hospital precertification or authorization. Without the authorization, the provider will be penalized with a reduction in benefits, which he or she cannot collect from the patient.

For specific conditions and treatment, physicians are required to obtain preauthorization for patient care for outpatient and inpatient services before beginning psychiatric care or treatment. This authorization must be obtained from the main office in Detroit, Michigan.

When a physician fails to comply with this request, benefits are greatly reduced for services. This reduction in benefit cannot be passed along to the patient. For continued disregard of the rules and regulations for preauthorization, the physician could be subjected to sanctions against the practice by the local Blue Shield office.

It is important to remember that under this program, while all authorization must come from the main office in Detroit, claims must be filed to the Blue Shield office for the state in which services were rendered.

Ford Motor Company Program. Ford Motor Company is self-insured, but it has a contract with Blue Shield to underwrite the program. All claims follow the same guidelines as stated for UCR providers for each state where the service is rendered. Like the Chrysler plan, Ford offers different coverage packages and most company contracts comply with the central certification benefit package.

General Motors Program. One of the largest accounts utilizing the NASCO system is General Motors (GM). General Motors is self-insured but underwritten by Blue Shield of Michigan. In order to provide better, uninterrupted coverage for retired members of the GM community, GM made one important change in the payment policy for retired personnel. Unlike most companies that switch payment policies regarding primary and secondary payers, GM Blue Shield is always primary to Medicare benefits.

When an employee is covered under the retirement portion of the program, the physician's office should file claims to Blue Shield as the primary insurance. Blue Shield will make payment according to the Blue Shield contract and then cross the claim over to Medicare for any additional payments. This payment program allows the physician to receive more payment benefit for services than he or she normally would receive if Medicare had been the primary carrier for the patient because Blue Shield reimbursement is generally higher than that of most Medicare programs.

General Motors Informed Choice Plan (ICP)—A National Contract. General Motors employees, retirees, surviving spouses (primary enrollees), and their eligible dependents (secondary enrollees) are enrolled in one of four options offering health care coverage within the ICP. A general overview is provided to their enrollees, followed by a more detailed discussion of specific plan provisions.

The ICP gives health care professionals, the Blue Cross and Blue Shield Plan, and GM enrollees an opportunity to work together to maintain quality care while reducing health care costs. Patients selecting the informed choice insurance option are subject to strict utilization management controls governing all nonmaternity elective admissions and emergency admissions. General Motors has informed its employees that *it is the responsibility of the physicians and/or the provider to secure and comply with the "predetermination provisions" of the health benefit package*.

For all services provided to BC/BS patients, providers must seek a predetermination of the medical necessity of each GM-covered inpatient admission or risk nonpayment or payment reduction for services provided. Preauthorization of services is administered by BC/BS of Michigan.

Traditional Insurance Option

The traditional insurance option generally provides the same scope of benefits available to enrollees through their previous Blue Cross and Blue Shield coverage. However, full benefits for inpatient hospital services will be provided only after predetermination approval.

Members covered under the PPO option use the local plan's PPO network, while HMO members may have different plans depending on where they live. Mental health and substance abuse coverage information is provided at the bottom of the enrollee's identification card.

Medicare

Background Information

Medicare is the federal government's health insurance program created by Title XVIII of the Social Security Amendment of 1965 titled "Health Insurance for the Aged and Disabled." The Medicare program is divided into two parts: Part A and Part B.

The Part A portion of Medicare, also called Hospital Insurance (HI) for the Aged and Disabled, covers institutional providers for inpatient, hospice, and home health services.

The Part B portion, also called Supplementary Medical Insurance (SMI) Benefits for the Aged and Disabled, provides benefits for noninstitutional health care providers, most notably physician services. Table 2.1 defines Part B service coverage.

To be enrolled in the Medicare program, persons must be 65 or older, retired on Social Security benefits, the spouse of a person paying into the Social Security system, or those receiving Social Security Disability Benefits for a two-year period. Special eligibility allows coverage of those diagnosed with end-stage

Table 2.1   **Medicare (Part B): Medical Insurance-covered Services for 1998**

Services	Benefit	Medicare Pays	Patient Pays
Medical Expenses Physicians' services, Inpatient and outpatient medical and surgical services and supplies, physical and speech therapy, diagnostic tests, durable medical equipment, and other services	Unlimited if medically necessary	80% of approved amount (after $100 deductible); 50% of approved charges for most outpatient mental health services	$100 deductible, plus 20% of approved amount and limited charges above approved amount
Clinical Laboratory Services Blood tests, urinalysis, and more	Unlimited if medically necessary	Generally 100% of approved amount	Nothing for services
Home Health Care Part-time or intermittent skilled care, home health aide services, durable medical equipment and supplies, and other services	Unlimited as long as Medicare conditions are met	100% of approved amount; 80% of approved amount for durable medical equipment	Nothing for services; 20% of approved amount for durable medical equipment
Outpatient Hospital Treatment Services for the diagnosis or treatment of illness or injury	Unlimited if medically necessary	Medicare payment to hospital based on hospital cost	20% of billed amount (after $100 deductible)
Blood	Unlimited if medically necessary	80% of approved amount (after $100 deductible and starting with 4th pint)	First 3 pints plus 20% of approved amount for additional pints (after $100 deductible)

1998 Medicare Part B monthly premium: $43.80 (premium may be higher if patient enrolls late).

Once the patient has $100 of expenses for covered services in 1998, the Part B deductible does not apply to any further covered services received for the rest of the year.

renal disease (ESRD), the medical expenses of kidney donors to persons with ESRD, the spouses and dependent children of workers who paid into Social Security, and retired federal employees of the Civil Service Retirement System (CSRS) and their spouses. Everyone eligible for Social Security benefits is automatically enrolled in Part A, which covers institutional care. Beneficiaries are responsible for a deductible, co-payments, and monthly premiums.

Medicare Part B premiums are usually taken from the enrollee's monthly Social Security check. Enrollees who do not receive Social Security benefits can pay monthly premiums in order to receive Part B Medicare. Currently, the annual deductible is $100; however, the annual deductible is determined by Congress and changes periodically.

Medicare is administered by the HCFA, a federal agency in the Department of Health and Human Services (DHHS). The actual day-to-day operations are handled on a local basis by large regional insurance companies, such as Travelers, Cigna, or Blue Cross/Blue Shield plans, that have been awarded Medicare contracts. These companies are called Medicare carriers. Most of a physician's contact with Medicare will be through the local carrier's provider representative. All physicians and health care providers are required by law to bill Medicare for services rendered by completing the HCFA-1500 claim form at no charge to the patient.

When Medicare began on July 1, 1966, there were 19.1 million persons enrolled in the program. By the end of 1975, there were about 24 million enrollees; in 1985, almost 30 million enrollees; and in 1996, more than 38.1 million enrollees in Part B of the Medicare program.

Medicare Part B reimburses physician services according to the allowances defined in the Medicare Fee Schedule (MFS), which is based on the Resource Based Relative Value Scale (RBRVS). Under RBRVS, physician payment allowances for the same service may vary from one locality to another because of the localities' geographic practice cost index (GPCI); however, all physicians in the same locality, regardless of their specialty, receive the same payment for the same service. Payment variations for a Medicare service within a region depend on (1) whether the physician participates with Medicare, (2) the facility where the service is performed, and (3) whether the claim is assigned.

Understanding Medicare Participation

Each year, HCFA invites every physician to participate or discontinue participation by December 31. Medicare participation means that the physician agrees to accept assignment for all Medicare claims and to accept Medicare's allowable charge as payment in full for his or her services. Physicians who elect not to participate (referred to as "nonpar" physicians) can still accept assignment on a claim-by-claim basis.

The number of physicians electing to participate in Medicare has steadily increased over the past ten years.

Agreeing to participate means:

1. The physician agrees to accept assignment for all Medicare claims he or she submits. Assignment means the physician requests direct payment from Medicare. Medicare forwards the check with 80 percent payment to the physician.

2. The physician agrees to accept Medicare's allowable charge as payment in full for the services, regardless of the charge he or she makes. Note that Medicare determines the allowable charge, then reimburses the physician 80 percent of

that amount. The remaining 20 percent co-insurance and any unpaid amount of the annual $100 deductible are the patient's responsibility.

3. The physician agrees not to bill the patient for services determined by Medicare to be noncovered services or certain elective procedures. However, the physician may bill the patient for other noncovered services provided notice of noncoverage was provided before the services were rendered.

Electing not to participate with Medicare means the physician has the choice, on a claim-by-claim basis, to accept assignment.

Payments to nonparticipating (nonpar) physicians on assigned claims are 5 percent less than payments to participating physicians. For example, if the fee schedule amount for participating physicians is $100, the amount paid to a nonparticipating physician's assigned claim will be $95.

For unassigned claims, the physician must adhere to *limiting charge* limitations, also referred to as balance billing limits, determined by Medicare. Violation of the charge limitations is considered a violation of Medicare regulations. Physicians can obtain the limiting charge amounts from their local Medicare carriers.

Advantages and Disadvantages of Participation

1. Effective September 1, 1990, *regardless of the assignment status* of a claim or the participation status of a physician, *all physicians must submit bills to Medicare* on behalf of their patients. What used to be an advantage for nonparticipating physicians has equalized, resulting in the same time and costs to all practices.

2. On assigned claims, reimbursement is sent directly to the practice. This guarantees at least partial payment and can simplify bookkeeping procedures for the staff. Additionally, the remittance advice received with the check provides important feedback to the practice in terms of accuracy of coding, coverage information, and regulatory information, which is vital to improving reimbursements. This important information is lost when the nonparticipating practice does not accept assignment on the claim.

   On unassigned claims, however, because payment can be collected "at time of service," the staff does not have to perform the extra record-keeping step of updating the file when the payment is received. The file can be marked *paid* at that time and put away, thus saving time, increasing efficiency, and possibly avoiding mistakes.

   Although the nonparticipating physician who does not accept assignment on a claim can collect the fee at the time of service, many do not. What this means for the practice is that the Medicare payment sent to the patient may be spent on something other than the physician's fee. Because collection is only as effective as the staff has time to make it, this could become a burdensome and costly process. At least for assigned claims, the only amount to be collected is the co-insurance and deductible amounts. The practice is assured it will receive at least part of the reimbursement.

3. Collection from the patient poses less of a problem for the participating physician. In many circumstances, collection from the patient is avoided as many Medicare enrollees carry supplemental insurance, which pays for some or all deductible and co-insurance balances. Most carriers have an arrangement whereby they will send the necessary information to the appropriate supplemental insurer, thus eliminating this process for the office staff or the patient. (This advantage is usually only available to participating physicians.) Even though the practice must collect from two sources, it does usually collect.

   For a nonparticipating physician who does not accept assignment, the fee can be collected at the time of service—that means no waiting, speedy cash flow, and no cost of collection. But again, if the fee is not collected from the patient at the time of service, the practice runs the risk of collecting substantially less money or no money at all from the patient and must cover the cost and time of collection efforts. Also, subsequent medical necessity denials cause the practice to have to refund any amounts previously collected to the patient.

4. Nonparticipating physicians have additional requirements that participating physicians do not, such as the completion of the elective surgery advance notice form.

5. Carriers maintain and distribute a listing of all participating physicians, groups, and clinics. This annual listing, called the Medicare Participation Directory or MEDPARD, contains the names, addresses, and phone numbers of all physicians, groups, and clinics that have elected participation for a calendar year. The vast distribution of MEDPARD could help increase the participating physician's patient base.

6. When referring a Medicare patient to a nonparticipating physician for outpatient care, hospitals are required to also provide, where practical, the name of a participating physician qualified to perform the same services.

7. Medicare includes on all EOMB statements for unassigned claims a statement reminding the patient about the participation program. Some carriers point out the amount of money the patient could have saved with a participating provider.

8. While this consideration may not be paramount to all practices, it is important to think about how physicians' participation status affects physicians'

Medicare patients. Many Medicare beneficiaries do not understand the participation program or assignment agreement, and an explanation does not always help them understand it better. Participation removes a burden from these patients, possibly helping them focus on getting well rather than worrying about how to pay for it.

Medicare Outpatient Deductibles and Co-payment

The 1998 Medicare Part B outpatient deductible is $100 per year, and the beneficiary co-insurance responsibility is 20 percent of the MFS payment allowance. However, the payment rules vary based on physician participation status and whether the claim was taken under assignment.

If a participating physician charges $100 for a service and the participating allowance is $60, Medicare will reimburse directly to the physician 80 percent of $60, or $48. The patient is responsible for 20 percent of $60, or $12, and the remaining $40 in excess of the allowance will be written off as a Medicare participation contractual allowance.

Under the same scenario, except for a nonparticipating physician not accepting assignment, the MFS has a nonparticipating limiting charge allowance that is calculated at 115 percent of the participating allowance. This limiting charge value represents the charge amount the nonparticipating physician cannot exceed when billing Medicare beneficiaries without facing possible Medicare fines and penalties.

The limiting charge for the service with the $60 participating allowance is equal to (115 percent x $60) or $69. So, the nonparticipating physician's charge cannot exceed $69. When billed to Medicare at $69, Medicare pays 95 percent of the 80 percent or $52.44. The beneficiary is responsible for 20 percent of the allowance or $13.80, plus the nonparticipating physician can collect the balance of the $69 charge ($69 minus [$52.44 + $13.80], or $2.76) from the patient.

Coordination of Benefits—Medicare as Secondary Payer

Basically, the Medicare Secondary Payer (MSP) program's function is to coordinate the coverage of health benefits between the Medicare program and other health insurers, with particular emphasis on employer group health plans.

Services payable under workers' compensation plans or the Federal Black Lung Program, or authorized by the Veterans Affairs, have always been excluded from primary payment under Medicare, but may coordinate secondary payer benefits.

Exhibit 2.3   Sample MSP Admission Questionnaire

<u>MEDICARE SECONDARY PAYER QUESTIONNAIRE</u>

Part I

1. Is the patient receiving Black Lung (BL) benefits? _____ yes _____ no
BL IS PRIMARY ONLY FOR CLAIMS RELATED TO BL.

2. Has the Department of Veteran Affairs (DVA) authorized and agreed to pay for care at this facility?____yes (DVA IS PRIMARY FOR THESE SERVICES) _____ no.

3. Was the illness/injury due to a work-related accident/condition? _____ yes _____ no
If YES, record date of Injury/Illness. WC IS PRIMARY PAYER ONLY FOR CLAIMS RELATED TO WORK RELATED INJURIES OR ILLNESSES. **GO TO PART III**   If NO, **GO TO PART II.**

Part II

1. Was illness/injury due to a non-work related accident? ___ yes ___ no If NO, **GO TO PART III.**

2. What type of accident caused the illness/injury?___automobile___non-automobile
NO FAULT INSURER IS PRIMARY PAYER FOR THOSE CLAIMS RELATED TO THE ACCIDENT. GO TO PART III.

3. Was another party responsible for this accident? _____ yes _____ no
LIABILITY INSURER IS PRIMARY ONLY FOR THOSE CLAIMS RELATED TO THE ACCIDENT. GO TO PART III

Part III

1. Is the beneficiary entitled to Medicare based on:
___Age. **Go to Part IV** ___Disability. **Go to Part V** ___ESRD. **Go to Part VI**

Part IV – Working Aged

1. Does the patient have current employment status? _____ yes _____ no

2. Does the patient's spouse have current employment status? _____ yes _____ no
IF PATIENT ANSWERED NO TO BOTH NUMBERS 1 & 2, MEDICARE IS PRIMARY UNLESS THE PATIENT ANSWERED YES TO QUESTIONS IN PART I OR II. DO NOT PROCEED ANY FURTHER.

3. Does the patient have Group Health Plan (GHP) coverage based on his/her own or a spouse's current employment status?
___yes ___no If NO, STOP. **MEDICARE IS PRIMARY PAYER UNLESS THE PATIENT ANSWERED YES TO QUESTIONS IN PART I OR II.**

4. Does the employer that sponsors the patient's GHP employ 20 or more employees?___ yes ____ no
If YES, **GROUP HEALTH PLAN IS PRIMARY**
If NO, STOP. MEDICARE IS PRIMARY UNLESS THE PATIENT ANSWERED YES TO QUESTIONS IN PART I OR II.

Part V – Disability

1. Does the patient have current employment status? ____ yes _____ no If No, record date of retirement.

2. Does a family member of the patient have current employment status? __ yes __ no If No, record date of retirement. **IF THE PATIENT ANSWERED NO TO BOTH NUMBERS 1 & 2, MEDICARE IS PRIMARY UNLESS THE PATIENT ANSWERED YES TO QUESTIONS IN PART I OR II. DO NOT PROCEED ANY FURTHER.**

3. Does the patient have GHP coverage based on his/her or family's employment status? ___ yes ___ no
If NO, STOP. MEDICARE IS PRIMARY UNLESS THE PATIENT ANSWERED YES TO QUESTIONS IN PART I OR II.

4. Does the employer that sponsors the patient's GHP employ 100 or more employees?___ yes _____ no
If YES, **GROUP HEALTH PLAN IS PRIMARY.**
If No, STOP. MEDICARE IS PRIMARY UNLESS THE PATIENT ANSWERED YES TO QUESTIONS IN PART I OR II.

Part VI – ESRD

1. Does the patient have group health plan coverage? _____ yes _____ no
If No, **STOP. MEDICARE IS PRIMARY.**

2. Is the patient within the 30-month coordination period?__ yes ___ no **STOP. MEDICARE IS PRIMARY.**

3. Is the patient entitled to Medicare on the basis of either ESRD and age or ESRD and disability? ___yes ___no. STOP. **GHP IS PRIMARY DURING THE 30-MONTH COORDINATION PERIOD.**

4. Was the patient's initial entitlement of Medicare (including simultaneous entitlement) based on ESRD? ___yes **STOP GHP CONTINUES TO PAY PRIMARY DURING THE 30-MONTHS.**
___no. **INITIAL ENTITLEMENT IS BASED ON AGE OR DISABILITY.**

5. Does the working aged or MSP disability provision apply (i.e. Is the GHP primary based on the age or disability entitlement)?___yes **STOP. GHP CONTINUES TO PAY PRIMARY DURING 30-MONTH COORDINATION PERIOD.** ___no **MEDICARE CONTINUES TO PAY PRIMARY.**

IT IS IMPORTANT TO REMEMBER TO ACQUIRE DATES AND INFORMATION RELATING TO EMPLOYMENT AND BENEFITS COVERAGE. THIS INFORMATION WOULD INCLUDE RETIREMENT, ACCIDENT, AND START DATES FOR BENEFITS AS WELL AS NAME AND ADDRESS OF INSURANCE CARRIERS AND EMPLOYERS, POLICY OR IDENTIFICATION NUMBERS, GROUP IDENTIFICATION NUMBERS, NAME OF POLICY HOLDER, RELATIONSHIP TO PATIENT, AND CLAIM NUMBERS.

There are four types of insurance coverage circumstances that make Medicare benefits (payments) secondary to other forms of insurance. They include coverage by:

1. Employer Group Health Plans (EGHP) insurance for working aged beneficiaries over 65 or the spouse of an employed individual of any age, and the beneficiary is covered under an EGHP

2. Liability or "no-fault" insurance for automobile, homeowners, or property claims that provide personal injury or medical expense coverage

3. Disability insurance for beneficiaries under age 65 and disabled, who are covered by a large group health plan (LGHP)

4. Work-related illness/injury insurance such as workers' compensation, Black Lung, or the Veterans Affairs

The reporting of Medicare as secondary payer has been mandated by HCFA; therefore, physicians must take an active role in the identification of MSP claims before billing Medicare as primary. This can be accomplished by having the patient fill out the MSP questionnaire, which asks a series of questions about the four categories of "other" insurers (see Exhibit 2.3).

Both the MSP questionnaire and billing procedures for each of the four circumstances have been published in most of the Medicare carrier newsletters. Practices that fail to follow MSP requirements will experience Medicare denials, accumulated accounts receivable, irritated beneficiaries, and less than optimal reimbursement.

If physicians determine the beneficiary has EGHP insurance that makes Medicare the secondary payer, physicians must bill the private insurance first for all the services and supplies provided during the patient encounter. Because Medicare is not the patient's primary insurer, physicians are not obligated to bill the physicians' "Medicare rates" or limiting charges, nor are physicians obligated to abide by Medicare service and supply coverage limits, unless so defined by the primary insurer. Physicians should bill their standard or private insurance charges.

The Opportunity for Additional MSP Reimbursement   Practices unfamiliar with the MSP program assume that if the primary insurance payments exceed the Medicare allowable(s) for services rendered, the billing and collection process has been completed. This assumption not only prevents Medicare from tracking beneficiary coordination of benefits, deductible, and co-insurance liabilities, but also reduces legitimate payment optimization efforts.

How Much Medicare Will Pay as Secondary   The amount of the Medicare secondary payment (per service) is based on several factors. Medicare will pay the lowest of the following values:

1. The billed charge minus the primary insurer's payment

2. The amount Medicare would have paid as primary (that is, 80 percent of the MFS allowable amount)

3. The higher of (*a*) the fee schedule amount or (*b*) the other insurer's approved charge minus the amount the other insurer actually paid

What Can the Patient Be Charged?

If the claim is assigned, the beneficiary's obligation remains 20 percent as a co-insurance plus any unmet deductible. The physician can charge the patient only if the primary insurer's payment is less than the patient's Medicare co-insurance and deductible.

The patient's co-insurance (20 percent times $125) of $25 cannot be collected from the patient, as the primary payment ($120) satisfies this obligation. If the primary payment does not satisfy the beneficiary's obligation (that is, the primary payment was only $20), the physician can bill up to the deductible and co-insurance due, or $5.

Expenses that meet the beneficiary's Part B $100 deductible are credited to the deductible even if the primary insurer paid the entire bill and there is no Medicare benefit payable. The Part B deductible is credited on the basis of Medicare allowable charges, rather than the amount paid by the primary insurer.

Medicare Health Insurance ID Card

A sample of the Medicare Beneficiary Health Insurance ID card is shown below.

Exhibit 2.4   Medicare Beneficiary Health Insurance ID Card

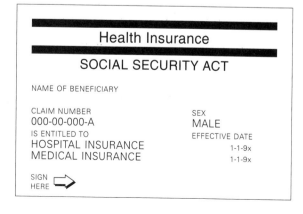

The Medicare ID card has four key areas to understand and utilize for efficient claim submission:

1. Beneficiary name

2. Medicare beneficiary health insurance claim number (HICN). This is the beneficiary's unique identification number. It matches his or her nine-digit Social Security number, plus a one- or two-digit alphanumeric modifier (discussed later)

3. Entitlement. This defines what the beneficiary is entitled to. "Hospital Insurance" indicates the beneficiary has Part A—hospital benefits. "Medical Insurance" indicates the beneficiary has Part B—outpatient benefits

4. Effective dates. This defines the effective date for each benefit. Medicare will not pay for services before these dates

Common HICN Suffix Modifiers

A:	Wage Earner	B:	Aged Wife
B1:	Husband	C1:	Children
D:	Aged Widow	D4:	Remarried Widow
E:	Mother (widow)	F1:	Father
F2:	Mother		

Other Medicare Claim Submission Policies

- Physicians must submit professional service claims on behalf of beneficiaries treated on the HCFA-1500 form. Electronic submission can also be used. Failure to bill on behalf of beneficiaries may be subject to a civil monetary penalty of up to $2,000 per violation.

- Physicians may not charge for preparing or filing Medicare claims.

- Medicare-assigned claims must be filed within one year from the date of service or the payment will be reduced by 10 percent. If the date of service was in October, November, or December, a practice has until the following December to submit the claim without the 10 percent payment reduction.

- It is the responsibility of physicians to accurately report the level or type of service they provide to patients according to the coding guidelines and reimbursement rules of the AMA and HCFA. Always refer to the Medicare Part B Bulletin for the latest coding changes and implementation dates.

How to File Primary Insurance if Not Medicare

- Bill all services, procedures, and supplies to the primary insurer and bill the full charge amount (standard rates).

- Identify Medicare as the secondary payer on the HCFA-1500 form.

- Items 11 a–d of the HCFA-1500 form: Enter primary insurance information.

- Items 9 a–d of the HCFA-1500 form: Enter Medicare as the secondary payer.

- Wait to receive primary EOB with payments and/or denials before billing Medicare. In some instances electronic billing may benefit from tape-to-tape transfers.

How to File a Medicare Secondary Claim

- After receiving the EGHP primary insurance EOB for partial payment, full payment, or denials for services rendered, bill Medicare.

- If the primary insurer has not paid the bill in full, prepare a claim for Medicare showing the full charges for the services. (The full charge cannot exceed the limiting charge on a nonassigned claim to Medicare.)

- Attach a copy of the primary insurance EOB or a copy of the check. The documentation should reflect primary allowed and payment amounts.

- Mark or stamp in red "Medicare Secondary Payer." **Note:** Electronic billers must file a paper claim when Medicare is the MSP.

- Complete the HCFA-1500 form:

  — Items 11 a–d: Enter beneficiary's information.

  — Items 9 a–d: Enter primary insurer information.

  — Enter the amount paid by the primary insurer.

  — See Chapter 4 for detailed instructions on completing a HCFA-1500 form.

Medicare Relationship to Other Health Insurance Programs

- **Commercial Insurance.** Commercial insurance is always primary to any public program, including CHAMPUS and Medicare. Therefore, beneficiaries age 65 or older who are covered by an employer health plan should use the commercial as the primary insurer.

- **Medicaid.** As a general rule of thumb, a state program is superseded by a federal program. So, if a person is eligible for Medicaid as well as Medicare, Medicare is usually the primary payer source. Further, all claims must be submitted assigned.

- **Workers' Compensation.** Expenses for medical care related to job-connected illness or injury are always paid by the workers' compensation program as primary.

- **Private Automobile Insurance.** Any claims arising out of an automobile accident or other personal injury claims are always payable as primary under a policy of automobile insurance and may be subject to recovery under the Federal Claims Collections Act.

When filing claims to Medicare as the primary payer, a number of different RBRVS-related payment policies may alter the traditional 80/20 payment split. An overview of special RBRVS payment policies is discussed in the next section.

Medicare Managed Care (Part C)

The Balanced Budget Act of 1997 created new health care options called *Medicare + Choice* (or *Medicare Plus Choice*). Under Medicare + Choice, HCFA contracts with managed care plans or provider service organizations to provide Medicare benefits. When beneficiaries enroll in Medicare managed care plans, they select a doctor from the plan's list of primary care physicians, and their primary care physician is then responsible for coordinating all of their health care needs.

The managed care plans are reimbursed by HCFA, according to an adjusted average per capita cost (AAPCC). The AAPCC is the estimated average fee-for-service cost of Medicare benefits for an individual by county of residence. It is based on the following factors: age, sex, institutional status, Medicaid, disability, and end-stage renal disease (ESRD) status. The AAPCC is the monthly capitation payment that will be made to the managed care plans. The provider is then at risk for all care of the patient. There may be some contractual exclusions, such as ESRD programs.

Medicare + Choice will increase the number of options beneficiaries can choose from to receive benefits. Beneficiaries can choose to receive their care through the traditional Medicare fee-for-service (RBRVS) program, or receive their care from managed care organizations that have "risk" contracts with Medicare. The new choices will become available at the end of 1998 and into 1999.

How Managed Care Works   Medicare's managed care plans work like traditional HMO plans. Though committed to providing members with quality health care, managed care plans generally maintain some control over important health care decisions. They also can limit access to specialists and intervene in other medical decisions. Managed care plans contract with Medicare to provide all of Medicare's benefits.

Managed care plans generally cover more services and have fewer out-of-pocket costs than fee-for-service. In addition to offering all statutory Medicare benefits, many plans promote preventive health care by providing extra benefits. Some of these benefits are eye examinations, hearing aids, routine physicals, and scheduled inoculations for little or no extra fee, as well as offering help with prescription drugs—and there is little or no paperwork in a managed care plan.

Each plan has its own network of hospitals, skilled nursing facilities, home health agencies, physicians, and other professionals. Depending on how the plan is organized, services are usually provided either at one or more centrally located health facilities, or in the private practice offices of the physicians and other health care professionals who are part of the plan.

Types of Managed Care Plans   Medicare offers two types of managed care contracts—"risk" and "cost" contracts. Here are some of the important differences:

- **Risk Plans.** These plans typically have "lock-in" requirements. This means that beneficiaries generally must receive all covered care through the plan or through referrals from the plan. If services that are not authorized by the plan are received, neither the plan nor Medicare will pay.

- **Cost Plans.** Cost plans do not have "lock-in" requirements. If beneficiaries enroll in a cost plan, they can either go to health care providers affiliated with the plan or go outside the plan. If beneficiaries go outside the plan, the plan probably will not pay but Medicare will.

If beneficiaries go outside of the plan, Medicare will pay its share of approved charges. Beneficiaries will be responsible for Medicare's co-insurance, deductibles, and other charges, just as if they were receiving care under the fee-for-service system. Because of this flexibility, a cost plan may be a good choice for beneficiaries if they travel frequently, live in another state part of the year, or want to use a doctor who is not affiliated with a plan.

Because Part C is relatively new, look for more details in the future. For more information, access the Medicare managed care comparison database "Medicare Compare," at the HCFA web site (www.medicare.gov).

Compliance Issues Concerning Medicare Billing

Because of the size and scope of the Medicare program, the government has several agencies and programs in place to identify and eliminate fraud, abuse, and program waste. Medicare, like the health care industry as a whole, has focused on the use of "compliance" programs to police providers, who, in turn, need to be policing themselves.

There have been laws and regulations that deal with fraud and abuse—the False Claims Act—on the books since before Medicare's inception. However, the Justice Department has recently stated that health care fraud and abuse is their number two priority, second only to violent crime. As a result of this priority, the government has increased the number and severity of current laws that impact physicians and have added civil penalties and penalties that can cause billing errors to result in penalties of over $10,000 per claim.

While the topic of compliance is a book unto itself, some of the billing issues that practices need to be aware of when billing Medicare include, but are not limited to:

- Reassignment of payment
- Limiting charges (nonparticipating)
- Correct CPT code assignment and service utilization
- Diagnostic coding and medical necessity
- "Incident-to" billing for physician assistants and nurse practitioners, and other ancillary employees of the practice
- Evaluation and management and CPT documentation guidelines
- Ancillary orders and supervision requirements
- Teaching physician and resident billing
- Routine waiver of co-payments, deductibles, or professional courtesy discounts
- Stark I and II—antireferral and compensation regulations
- Credit balances
- Correct coding initiative edits

Medicare Supplemental (Medigap) Insurance

While Medicare Parts A and B cover many health care costs, beneficiaries will still have to pay Medicare's co-insurance and deductibles. There are also many medical services and items that Medicare does not cover.

Beneficiaries may purchase a Medicare supplemental insurance (Medigap) policy. Medigap is private insurance that is designed to help pay beneficiaries' Medicare cost-sharing amounts. There are ten standard Medigap policies, and each offers a different combination of benefits.

The best time to buy a policy is during a Medigap open enrollment period. For a period of six months from the date beneficiaries are first enrolled in Medicare Part B and are age 65 or older, beneficiaries have a right to buy the Medigap policy of their choice. That is the beneficiary's open enrollment period.

Beneficiaries cannot be turned down or charged higher premiums because of poor health if they buy a policy during this period. When the Medigap open enrollment period ends, beneficiaries may not be able to buy the policy of their choice. They may have to accept whatever Medigap policy an insurance company is willing to sell them.

If beneficiaries have Medicare Part B but are not yet 65, their six-month Medigap open enrollment period begins when they turn 65. However, several states (Connecticut, Maine, Massachusetts, Minnesota, New Jersey, New York, Oklahoma, Oregon, Pennsylvania, Virginia, Washington, and Wisconsin) require at least a limited Medigap open enrollment period for Medicare beneficiaries under 65.

The beneficiaries' state insurance counseling office can answer questions about Medicare and other health insurance information. That office can also answer questions about Medicare SELECT, another type of Medicare supplemental health insurance that is sold by insurance companies and HMOs throughout most of the country.

Medicare SELECT

Medicare SELECT is the same as standard Medigap insurance in nearly all respects. The only difference between Medicare SELECT and standard Medigap insurance is that each insurer has specific hospitals, and in some cases specific physicians, that beneficiaries must use, except in an emergency, in order to be eligible for full benefits. Medicare SELECT policies generally have lower premiums than other Medigap policies because of this requirement.

Regional Carriers for DMEPOS Claims

HCFA has selected four regional Medicare contractors to be designated as durable medical equipment carriers (DMERCs). The DMERCs are responsible for processing all claims for durable medical equipment, prosthetics, orthotics, and supplies (DMEPOS). The address where the patient resides more than six months of the year defines the regional carrier where claims should be directed.

Medicaid

Title XIX of the Social Security Act of 1965, referred to as Medicaid, is a jointly funded federal and state matching entitlement program that provides medical assistance for certain individuals and families with low incomes and resources.

Medicaid recipients increased from about 10 million in calendar year 1967 to a projected 37.5 million in fiscal year 1996, an increase of 275 percent. Dependent children rose from 9.8 million in 1985 to 18.2 million in 1996, an increase of 86 percent. Medicaid recipients as a percentage of the total civilian population have risen from 10.2 percent in 1990 to approximately 14 percent in 1996, an increase of more than 35 percent.

The portion of each state's Medicaid program that is paid by the federal government, known as the Federal Medical Assistance Percentage (FMAP), is determined annually by a formula that compares the state's average per capita income level with the national income average. By law, the FMAP cannot be lower than 50 percent nor greater than 83 percent. The wealthier states have a smaller share of their costs reimbursed. The FMAPs vary from 50 percent (paid to 11 states and Washington, D.C.) to 79.01 percent (to Mississippi), with the average federal share among all states being 57.5 percent.

The federal government also shares in the state's expenditures for administration of the Medicaid program. Most administrative costs are matched at 50 percent for all states. However, depending on the complexities and need for incentives for a particular service, higher matching rates are authorized for certain functions and activities.

Federal Medicaid payments to states have no set limit or cap. Rather, the federal government matches (at FMAP rates) the state payments for the mandatory services plus the optional services that the individual state decides to provide for eligible recipients. Reimbursement rates must be sufficient to enlist enough providers so that Medicaid care and services are available under the plan at least to the extent that such care and services are available to the general population in that geographic area.

Within broad national guidelines that the federal government provides, each of the states (1) establishes its own eligibility standards; (2) determines the type, amount, duration, and scope of services; (3) sets the rate of payment for services; and (4) administers its own program. Thus, Medicaid programs vary considerably from state to state and within each state over time.

Eligibility for Medicaid

To be eligible for federal funds, states are required to provide Medicaid coverage for most individuals who receive federally assisted income-maintenance payments, as well as for related groups not receiving cash payments. The following displays the mandatory Medicaid eligibility groups:

- Recipients of Aid to Families With Dependent Children (AFDC)

- Children under age six who meet the state's AFDC financial requirements or whose family income is at or below 133 percent of the federal poverty level (FPL)

- Pregnant women whose family income is below 133 percent of the FPL (services to the women are limited to pregnancy, complications of pregnancy, delivery, and three months of postpartum care)

- Infants up to age 1 and pregnant women not covered under the mandatory rules whose family income is no more than 185 percent of the FPL (the percentage of FPL is set by each state)

- Supplemental Security Income (SSI) recipients (or aged, blind, and disabled individuals in states that apply more restrictive eligibility requirements)

- Special protected groups (typically, individuals who lose their cash assistance from AFDC or SSI because of earnings from work or increased Social Security benefits, but who may keep Medicaid for a period of time)

- Recipients of adoption assistance and foster care who are under Title IV-E of the Social Security Act

- Certain Medicare beneficiaries (described later)

- All children born after September 30, 1983, in families with incomes at or below the FPL (they must be given full Medicaid coverage until age 19; this phases in coverage, so that by the year 2002, all poor children under age 19 will be covered)

States also have the option to provide Medicaid coverage for other "categorically needy" groups. These optional groups share characteristics of the mandatory groups, but the eligibility criteria are somewhat more liberally defined. The broadest optional groups that states may cover (and for which they will receive federal matching funds) under the Medicaid program include the following:

- Children under age 21 who meet the AFDC income and resource requirements but who otherwise are not eligible for AFDC

- Recipients of state supplementary income payments

- Institutionalized individuals with income and resources below specified limits

- Certain aged, blind, or disabled adults who have incomes above those requiring mandatory coverage, but below the FPL

- Persons receiving care under home and community-based waivers

- TB-infected persons who would be financially eligible for Medicaid at the SSI level (but only for TB-related ambulatory services and for TB drugs)

- "Medically needy" persons (described below)

The option to have a "medically needy" (MN) program allows states to extend Medicaid eligibility to additional qualified persons with significant health care expenses who have income in excess of the mandatory or optional categorically needy levels. Such persons may "spend down" to Medicaid eligibility by incurring medical and/or remedial care expenses to offset their "excess" income, thereby reducing it to a level below the maximum income allowed by that state's Medicaid plan. States may also allow families to establish eligibility for MN coverage by paying monthly premiums to the state in an amount equal to the difference between the threshold allowance for income eligibility and a family's income (reduced by any unpaid expenses incurred for medical care in previous months).

The MN Medicaid program does not have to be as extensive as the "categorically needy" program in a state, but there are certain requirements. If a state has any MN program, certain services must be provided as a minimum (the state may also choose to include additional services); and in any MN program, a state is required to provide coverage to certain persons (certain children under age 18 and pregnant women who are MN). A state may elect to provide eligibility to other MN persons: aged, blind, and/or disabled persons; caretaker relatives of children deprived of parental support and care; and certain other financially eligible children up to age 21. In 1993, 40 states had an MN program that provided at least some services for at least some recipient groups.

Medicaid does not provide medical assistance for all poor persons. Even under the broadest provisions of the federal statute, Medicaid does not provide health care services even for very poor persons unless they are in one of the groups designated above. Low income is only one test for Medicaid eligibility; assets and resources also are tested against established thresholds (as determined by each state, within federal guidelines).

Once eligibility for Medicaid is determined, coverage generally is retroactive to the third month prior to application. Medicaid coverage generally stops at the end of the month in which a person no longer meets the criteria of any Medicaid eligibility group. In addition to the Medicaid program, most states have additional "state-only" programs to provide medical assistance for specified poor persons who do not qualify for Medicaid. Federal matching funds are not provided for these state-only programs.

Scope of Medicaid Services

Title XIX of the Social Security Act requires that, in order to receive federal matching funds, a state must offer the following basic services to the categorically needy populations:

- Inpatient hospital services

- Outpatient hospital services

- Prenatal care

- Physician services

- Nursing facility (NF) services for people age 21 or older

- Home health care for persons eligible for skilled-nursing services

- Family planning services and supplies

- Rural health clinic services

- Laboratory and x-ray services

- Pediatric and family nurse practitioner services

- Nurse-midwife services

- Certain federally qualified ambulatory and health-center services

- Early and periodic screening, diagnostic, and treatment (EPSDT) services (under 21 years old)

States may also receive federal assistance for funding if they elect to provide other approved optional services. A few of the optional services under the Medicaid program include clinic services, nursing facility services for the aged and disabled, intermediate care facilities for the mentally retarded (ICFs/MR), optometrist services and eyeglasses, prescribed drugs, prosthetic devices, dental services, and TB-related ambulatory services and drugs for qualifying persons.

Physician Application and Participation

As with Medicare, physicians must make application to Medicaid and wait to receive a Medicaid physician ID number. Physicians who treat Medicaid patients must accept Medicaid's payment for services as payment in full. In most states, patients do not have a co-payment, and physicians are not allowed to balance bill the patient.

Practices that provide services to Medicaid patients from more than one state, such as practices on state borders, need to know about the coverage policies of the applicable states, as they can vary significantly.

Medicaid is a recipient program, meaning that benefit and coverage information varies month by month. Because most state Medicaid programs issue eligibility cards on a monthly basis to patients, it is advisable to review Medicaid patients' current status before scheduling and providing services. Photocopying these cards at each visit helps verify the patient's status.

Medicaid Coordination of Benefits

Basically, *Medicaid should be the payer of last resort in almost any situation.* In the case of the patient with both Medicare and Medicaid, Medicaid will often pay the Medicare Part B deductible, co-insurance, and monthly premium amounts.

Relationship to Other Health Insurance Programs

- **Medicare**. Medicaid is always secondary to Medicare.

- **Workers' Compensation**. Expenses for medical care related to job-connected illness or injury are paid by the workers' compensation program as primary.

- **Private Automobile Insurance**. Any amounts paid by commercial insurance arising out of an automobile accident when the claims are also payable as primary under a policy of automobile insurance may be subject to recovery under the Federal Claims Collections Act.

Medicaid Claim Submission

While each state Medicaid program has its own coverage and payment policies, the billing requirements for Medicaid are the same as those for Medicare. Most Medicaid programs accept the HCFA-1500 for physician services. However, Medicaid coverage is limited, and the need to correctly code both CPT and ICD-9-CM codes is very important. Some state programs offer electronic claim submission.

Providers need to apply for enrollment into the Medicaid program before claims for services can be rendered. Once enrolled, be sure to obtain the most recent Medicaid *Physician Billing Guide* from the physicians' state Medicaid office.

Carefully review the billing guidelines and special coding requirements relative to the services physicians presently bill for.

Claims for services should be mailed within four to six days after the date of service. Some state programs start to deny services if the claim is submitted after sixty or ninety days from the date of service. Failure to meet this objective may indicate billing problems.

It is best to define Medicaid recipients as a separate financial class in billing software to assist in account follow-up with the physicians' Medicaid office. Be sure to identify contact names for reimbursement assistance.

Medicaid Managed Care Programs

Like Medicare, many state Medicaid programs are administering managed care programs for their Medicaid recipients. Below is a table of states with comprehensive statewide health care reform demonstrations:

Table 2.2

States With Comprehensive Statewide Health Care Reform Demonstrations—June 30, 1997

State	State Medicaid Enrollment	Managed Care Enrollment	Percent Enrolled in Managed Care
Alabama	497,434	407,643	81.95%
Arizona	431,813	349,142	80.85%
Colorado	228,558	184,000	80.50%
Delaware	80,561	65,061	80.76%
District of Columbia	125,000	80,721	64.58%
Hawaii	166,725	135,200	81.09%
Minnesota	402,787	169,329	42.04%
Ohio	1,095,268	352,833	32.21%
Oklahoma	437,161	222,818	50.97%
Oregon	376,345	312,345	82.99%
Rhode Island	114,162	70,944	62.14%
Tennessee	1,188,570	1,188,570	100.00%
Vermont	96,985	22,946	23.66%
Totals	**5,241,369**	**3,561,552**	**67.95%**

CHAMPUS/CHAMPVA

Background Information

CHAMPVA—The Civilian Health and Medical Program of the Veterans Affairs is a health benefit program for the families of veterans with 100 percent service-connected disability, or the surviving spouse or children of a veteran who dies from a service-connected disability.

CHAMPUS—The Civilian Health and Medical Program of the Uniformed Services is a cost-sharing program for military families, retirees and their families, some former spouses, and survivors of deceased military members. The uniformed services include the Army, Navy, Air Force, Marine Corps, Coast Guard, Public Health Service, and the National Oceanic and Atmospheric Administration.

CHAMPUS shares the cost of most medical services from civilian providers, when beneficiaries are not able to get care from a military hospital or clinic. Service families are eligible to receive inpatient and outpatient care from uniformed service hospitals and clinics. The types of medical services available at uniformed service hospitals vary by facility, and hospitals serve active-duty service members first.

There are four categories of eligibility: active duty, dependents of active duty, retired, and dependents of retired. All categories, except active duty, are afforded care in a uniformed service facility on a space-available basis.

CHAMPUS is now called *TRICARE Standard* in most of the country.

TRICARE: The Basics   TRICARE is the Defense Department's regional managed health care program for service families. It is a combination of resources by the Army, Navy, and Air Force under a regional management. In the past, each service managed its resources independently under a central authority. This often resulted in duplication and misuse of resources. To overcome these problems, TRICARE is being implemented region-by-region throughout the country.

TRICARE offers families three choices: (1) TRICARE Prime, an HMO-type source of care that has very low costs; (2) TRICARE Extra, an expanded network of providers that offers reduced cost sharing, does not require enrollment, and can be used on a case-by-case basis; and (3) TRICARE Standard, which is the same as CHAMPUS, with the same benefits and cost-sharing structure. For more information on CHAMPUS, see their web site at www.ochampus.mil. Below is a brief description of each option.

TRICARE Prime   This is a voluntary enrollment option that is much like a civilian HMO. If members live in an area where TRICARE Prime is offered, they will enroll for a year at a time and normally receive care from within the Prime network of civilian and military providers.

Active-duty service members themselves will have automatic enrollment and will choose, or be assigned to, a primary care manager. Their families, and all others who are eligible, must take action if they want to enroll. Enrollment of newborns and newly adopted children in TRICARE Prime is automatic if another family member is enrolled (unless the sponsor specifies otherwise), but the children must be registered in DEERS (the Defense Enrollment Eligibility Reporting System) before their enrollment in TRICARE Prime becomes effective.

Active-duty families will not have to pay an annual enrollment fee. All others will, but there will be no annual deductibles, and the patient's share of the costs for services under Prime will be reduced. Members do not have to file claims when using TRICARE Prime network providers. Covered services will be like those of TRICARE Standard (formerly called CHAMPUS), plus additional preventive and primary care services. For example, physical screenings are covered at no charge under TRICARE Prime but are not covered under the other two health care options, TRICARE Extra and TRICARE Standard.

Members must choose, or will be assigned, a "primary care manager" from whom they will get most of their routine health care. TRICARE Prime enrollees also have what is called a point of service (POS) option. This means that they can choose to get nonemergency services without a referral from their primary care physician. However, if they decide to get care under the POS option, there is an annual deductible of $300 for an individual, or $600 for a family. After the deductible is satisfied, cost-share for POS care will be 50 percent of the TRICARE allowable charge. Members may also have to pay any additional charges by non-network providers—up to 15 percent above the allowable charge. They also may have to pay the entire bill when services are provided and, after a claim is filed, wait for reimbursement of the government's share of the costs.

TRICARE Extra   Under this option, members do not have to enroll or pay an annual fee. They can seek care from a provider who is part of the TRICARE network, get a discount on services, and pay reduced cost shares (5 percent below those of TRICARE Standard) in most cases. Members will not have to file any claims when using network providers. Members must meet the normal annual outpatient deductible ($50 for one person or $100 for a family for active-duty pay grades E-4 and below; or $150 for one person or $300 for a family for all other eligible persons), just as they would under TRICARE Standard.

TRICARE Standard   This option is what historically has been known as CHAMPUS. Just as under CHAMPUS, TRICARE Standard pays a share of the cost of covered health services that members obtain from a nonnetwork civilian health care provider. There is no enrollment in TRICARE Standard. The annual deductibles, cost shares, and benefits are the same as for CHAMPUS.

Members have the freedom to choose their provider of care, but their costs will be higher than with the other two TRICARE options. Members must file their own claim forms, and perhaps pay a little more for the care (up to 15 percent more than the allowable charge), if the provider seen does not participate in TRICARE Standard. If the provider does participate, he or she agrees to accept the TRICARE Standard allowable charge as the full fee for the care received.

Eligibility

The categories of individuals eligible for CHAMPUS/CHAMPVA benefits are as follows:

1. Spouses of active-duty members of the uniformed services

2. Children* of active-duty members

3. Members of the uniformed services receiving or entitled to receive retired, retainer, or equivalent pay based on duty in the service

4. Spouses of retirees

5. Children* of retirees

6. Widowers and widows of deceased active-duty members and deceased retirees who have not remarried

7. Children* of deceased active-duty members and deceased retirees

8. Ex-spouses who have valid ID cards

   * To be eligible, children must be unmarried and under the age of 21 (age 18 for CHAMPVA). Financial dependence is not required except for students and disabled children who have passed their 18th or 21st birthday. Dependent student children are eligible if they are full-time students and have obtained a valid ID card.

The CHAMPVA sponsor (the active or retired military member) is not eligible for CHAMPVA benefits but is eligible for care from the VA.

When an individual reaches age 65 and becomes Medicare Part A eligible, CHAMPUS benefits cease. If Social Security eligibility is not met, CHAMPUS benefits will be extended indefinitely.

An individual under the age of 65 who becomes Medicare Part A eligible because of a disability and who elects Medicare Part B coverage retains CHAMPUS as a secondary payer effective October 1, 1991. Disabled spouse and dependent children of active-duty service members would have Medicare Part A and CHAMPUS without the Medicare Part B requirement.

Eligibility Verification

The Department of Defense maintains a worldwide database on military family enrollment and eligibility through the Defense Enrollment Eligibility Reporting System. Patients and providers can verify eligibility by calling the appropriate center on the next page:

800 334-4162 (California only);

800 527-5602 (Alaska and Hawaii only);

800 538-9552 (all other states).

A currently valid uniformed services identification card is required to establish eligibility. Children under age 10 are not issued ID cards except under unusual circumstances. Their eligibility is established on the basis of either parent's ID card. A "yes" in block 15b on the back of the card indicates eligibility.

CHAMPVA beneficiaries are issued a CHAMPVA ID card after the Veterans Affairs determines eligibility (Exhibit 2.6). A copy of a sample CHAMPUS ID card is shown below (Exhibit 2.5).

Exhibit 2.5   Sample CHAMPUS ID card

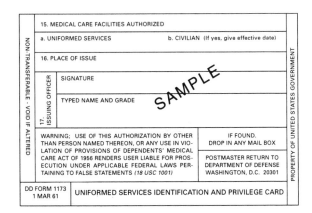

Exhibit 2.6   Sample CHAMPVA ID card

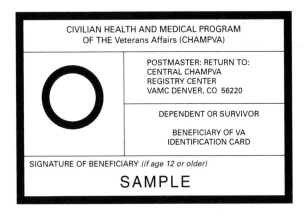

CHAMPUS Participation

As with Medicare, physicians must apply for and be approved by CHAMPUS in order for the patient to receive benefits for services. When the physician accepts assignment on a claim, he or she agrees to accept as payment the amount allowed by CHAMPUS, to write off the difference of the actual charge and the amount allowed by CHAMPUS, and to file the claim for the patient. The provider must collect any co-insurance amounts, noncovered items, or deductibles from the patient.

When the provider does not accept assignment, the practice may collect the full fee from the patient at the time service is rendered, is not bound by UCR agreements, and is not required to file claim forms.

Physicians who participate in the CHAMPUS program are expected to file insurance for the patient, write off the difference of the allowed amount (UCR) and the actual charge, and collect any outstanding co-payments and deductibles for the patient.

CHAMPUS operates on a fiscal year instead of a calendar year. The fiscal year runs from October 1 to September 30. That means that, beginning each October, the deductible amount of $150 per individual and $300 per family must be met before CHAMPUS will begin paying on claims.

Covered Benefits

CHAMPUS provides coverage for most medical and surgical conditions; contagious diseases; and nervous, mental, and chronic disorders, such as alcoholism and certain obesity surgeries. The program will pay a co-insurance for drugs prescribed by physicians or dentists when obtained from a pharmacy by written prescription. Any service considered to be experimental is not a covered benefit of the program. There are some medication benefits programs available that require co-payments and not co-insurance.

However, a few organ transplant operations are allowed, such as cornea, kidney, liver, and bone marrow, with some limitations imposed. Active-duty dependents only are eligible to receive one eye examination per year.

For psychiatric services, the provider should be aware that for a certain number of visits (for example, 33 for Missouri, 22 for Illinois), regardless of the number of times he or she actually saw the patient, an ongoing treatment report must be completed. Otherwise, the patient will not receive further benefits or reimbursement from CHAMPUS.

Claims should be submitted on Form 501 or HCFA-1500. Because of the detailed information required for a CHAMPUS claim, it is best to use Form 501 whenever possible.

Nonavailability Statement

Any CHAMPUS beneficiary who lives within the zip code catchment area of a uniformed services hospital must obtain a nonavailability statement (NAS) before CHAMPUS will share the cost of nonemergency inpatient care from a civilian source. The catchment area is defined by zip codes and is based on approximately a 40-mile radius surrounding the military medical facility.

Obtaining the NAS waiver is the responsibility of the patient. Without the waiver, services could be denied for payment by CHAMPUS. All civilian hospital admissions require a nonavailability waiver from the military facility before members who live within a catchment area surrounding a military medical facility are admitted.

There are 14 outpatient procedures that require an NAS before civilian care is rendered. These procedures are arthroscopy, breast mass or tumor excision, cataract removal, cystoscopy, dilation and curettage, gastrointestinal endoscopy, gynecologic laparoscopy, hernia repair, ligation or transection of fallopian tubes, myringotomy, neuroplasty, nose repair, strabismus repair, and tonsillectomy/adenoidectomy.

Services/Situations Requiring a Nonavailability Statement

A nonavailability statement is required in the following situations:

1. When the patient has been receiving care from an outpatient civilian source and it is medically advisable that care continue from the civilian physician or source

2. When there is no space available at the military facility

3. When the military facility does not maintain the necessary medical facilities or personnel required for care or treatment

4. When the patient resides outside the catchment area

5. When the patient is covered by another insurance policy that is the primary payer

Inpatient Deductible and Co-insurance

For active-duty spouses and children, there is a co-insurance amount each time a patient is admitted to a civilian hospital. The amount is the total amount that would have been charged if the admission had been to a uniformed services medical facility. The charge for inpatient care at these facilities changes each year and must be appropriately computed to determine the co-payments. This includes CHAMPVA, whichever is less. The current daily rate became effective October 1. There is no inpatient deductible.

Outpatient Deductible and Co-payment

Effective April 1, 1991, family members of enlisted grades (E1–E4) and family members of CHAMPVA beneficiaries are responsible for the first $50 for coverage of outpatient services and supplies during any fiscal year (October 1 through September 30). For two or more members of the same family, the deductible is not to exceed $100 per fiscal year. For all other categories of CHAMPUS beneficiaries (that is, retirees and their family members and family members of active-duty sponsors in grade E5 or above), the outpatient deductible is $150, not to exceed $300 per fiscal year.

CHAMPUS pays 80 percent of the CHAMPUS-determined reasonable charges for covered services and supplies received by spouses and children of active-duty members after the deductible has been met. After the deductible has been met, CHAMPUS pays 75 percent for covered services received by retirees, spouses and children of retirees, spouses and children of deceased active-duty members and deceased retirees, and CHAMPVA beneficiaries.

Coordination of Benefits (or Double Coverage)

Section 779 of Public Law 97-377, the FY83 Department of Defense Appropriations Act, changed the procedure for determining the primary payer in a double coverage situation. According to this law, *no CHAMPUS funds* "shall be available for the payment for any service or supply for persons enrolled in any other insurance, medical service, or health plan to the extent that the service or supply is a benefit under the other plan."

In other words, CHAMPUS is the secondary payer to *all* other insurance, medical service, or health plan in all cases. This law was effective on December 21, 1982. Active-duty families no longer have the option to file with CHAMPUS first. The exclusionary clause for policies in effect before 1966 is no longer in existence, and private plans are also included as double-coverage situations.

Relationship to Other Government Programs

- **Medicare**. CHAMPUS-eligible dependents of active-duty sponsors with Medicare Part A maintain CHAMPUS as the secondary payer. Non-active-duty dependents under age 65 with a disability maintain CHAMPUS as the secondary payer if they have Medicare Parts A and B.

- **Medicaid**. If a person is eligible for Medicaid as well as CHAMPUS benefits, CHAMPUS always pays first.

- **Workers' compensation**. Expenses for medical care related to job-connected illness or injury that are paid by the workers' compensation program, or can be paid by such a program, are not covered by CHAMPUS. Only if benefits are exhausted under the workers' compensation program would CHAMPUS then assume responsibility for the balance.

- **Private insurance or automobile insurance**. Any amounts paid by CHAMPUS arising out of an automobile accident when these same amounts are also payable, in whole or in part, under a policy of automobile insurance may be subject to recovery under the Federal Claims Collections Act. Commercial insurance also supersedes CHAMPUS as primary except under certain coverage conditions.

The CHAMPUS/CHAMPVA billing address:

WPS–CHAMPUS/CHAMPVA
P.O. Box 7889
Madison, WI 53707-7891

The CHAMPUS/CHAMPVA correspondence address:

WPS–CHAMPUS/CHAMPVA Inquiry
P.O. Box 7927
Madison, WI 53707-7927

CHAMPUS/CHAMPVA appeals

P.O. Box 8607
Madison, WI 53708-8607
The toll-free number for providers' use is 800 866-6337

CHAMPVA

The Civilian Health and Medical Program of the Veterans Affairs (CHAMPVA) was created in 1973 to provide a medical benefits program for spouses and children of veterans with total, permanent, service-connected disabilities or for the surviving dependents of veterans who die as a result of service-connected disabilities. Members who receive CHAMPUS benefits do not qualify for coverage under CHAMPVA.

Dependent eligibility for benefits is determined by the Veterans Affairs (VA). The prospective recipient must go to the nearest VA hospital or clinic to be reviewed for eligibility in the program. If the person is eligible for CHAMPVA benefits, the VA will issue the recipient a CHAMPVA identification card.

The benefits under the CHAMPVA program are similar to the benefits of members who are dependents of retired or deceased military personnel in the CHAMPUS program. CHAMPVA recipients have the same cost-sharing portions as retirees in the CHAMPUS program.

CHAMPVA claims should be submitted to CHAMPUS hospital contractors and fiscal administrators. Claims should be submitted on a UB-92 claim form or HCFA-1450 form for hospital billing and Form 501 for physician services.

Alternate Health Plans

In addition to the traditional plans discussed earlier, several alternative systems have come into prominence over the past few decades. These include health maintenance organizations (HMOs), preferred provider organizations (PPOs), independent practice associations (IPAs), physician/hospital organizations (PHOs), point-of-service plans (POSs), and self-funded plans. Most commercial and Blue Cross/Blue Shield programs offer one or more of these alternatives. Each is discussed below.

Health Maintenance Organizations (HMOs)

Health maintenance organizations (HMOs) provide comprehensive health care ranging from physician services to hospitalization. Patients enrolled in an HMO pay a fixed amount per month or other payment period. Enrollment entitles them to the full range of services offered by the HMO during the period of enrollment. An HMO can be viewed as a combination of a health insurer and a health care delivery system. Many commercial and BC/BS plans offer HMOs as an alternative to standard service contracts or indemnity plans.

HMO Operations/Patient Entitlements   Because HMOs are paid a fixed amount regardless of services provided, they generally attempt to reduce and control costs of health care delivery through utilization review, ambulatory surgery versus inpatient surgery, second opinions, and preventive medicine.

Enrollees are instructed to use only "panel" or "participating" physicians, hospitals, ancillary centers, etc., with which the HMO has a contracted arrangement. The patient may face financial responsibility for out-of-network charges. HMOs also save administrative costs through subcontracting key functions such as benefit communications management, physician enrollment and credentialing, claims processing, utilization review, and remittance management.

In an HMO program, the patient is usually responsible for a small co-payment, ranging from $5 to $25, for visits to the physician. The patient has a selected group of physicians from which he or she may seek care. Should a patient elect to see a physician who does not participate in the HMO network, the patient may forfeit all benefits for those services. If the patient is admitted to a non-HMO hospital, the patient may not receive any benefits for the hospital bill nor will the physician receive payment even though he or she is an HMO provider of service. However, in an emergency, the patient will usually have 24 hours in which to transfer to an HMO facility unless it is a life-threatening situation.

While there are four different HMO types or "models," they share the common characteristic of operations, capitated reimbursement, and control over health care delivery and financing. The major differences between the models involve the relationship between the HMO and its participating physicians. Each model type is discussed below.

Staff Model HMOs   Staff model HMOs employ physicians who are typically paid a fixed salary to provide services to HMO beneficiaries. Staff models are considered "closed-panel" HMOs because physicians must be members of the HMO. Staff models have a greater degree of control over the practice patterns of physicians, so the staff model may limit physician autonomy. As a result, HMOs can more easily manage and control utilization of health services.

Group Model HMOs   Group model HMOs primarily contract with larger, multispecialty physician groups; therefore, the physicians are employees of the group practice and not the HMO. Group models are also considered "closed panel" because physicians must be members of the group to gain access to HMO patients. The group model physician has more autonomy than does a staff model physician, but he or she must still adhere to internal utilization review and service cost goals set by the group practice to meet practice-wide goals.

There are two categories of group model HMOs—the captive group and the independent group. They are differentiated by the amount of non-HMO work provided by a contracted multispecialty practice.

In a *captive group model* HMO, the physician group exists solely to provide services to the HMO exclusively. The group does not serve non-HMO clients. In most cases, these HMO models have formed the group practice to serve its members, recruit physicians, and provide administrative support services to the physicians. The most prominent example of a captive group model is the Kaiser

Foundation Health Plan, where the permanent medical groups provide all physician services to Kaiser's members.

In an *independent group model HMO,* the HMO contracts with an existing multispecialty group practice, and, in many cases, the group practice is the sponsor or owner of the HMO. An example of an independent group HMO is the Geisinger Health Plan of Danville, Pennsylvania, for which services are provided by the Geisinger Clinics. Independent groups, as their name suggests, often serve other contracts and patients in addition to the HMO members.

Individual Practice Association (IPA) Model   IPA models contract with independent physician groups for all specialties. The IPA is a separate legal entity of which physicians are members, but each practice retains its own office, staff, and physician identity. It also assumes risks associated with patient care.

IPA HMOs recruit physicians from all specialties so they can offer a complete package of services while minimizing the need to refer to out-of-plan physicians. While there may be more physician autonomy under IPAs, control over utilization and cost is much more difficult to manage. In addition, the IPA attempts to transfer financial risk back to the member practice and not the plan.

While the physician compensation arrangements vary from IPA to IPA, the HMO usually pays a fixed amount per subscriber (a capitation fee) to the IPA. The IPA in turn pays the member physicians, usually on a fee-for-service basis, as services are rendered to the HMO patients. Some plans may pay the primary care physicians under a capitated arrangement and pay the specialists on a discounted fee-for-service arrangement, or vice versa. Subcapitation is where the specialist is paid on a capitated basis. Since the specialists account for 80 percent of the costs, some programs have reversed capitation, where the specialist is capitated and the primary care physician receives a fee for service. The incentive is for the primary care physician to do more. HMOs have had to become more aggressive and creative in their compensation arrangements to achieve and maintain high quality of care and access to physicians of all specialties.

IPA physicians are paid from the pool of capitation funds. This provides them with an incentive to contain costs associated with the provision of care. That is, if the funds are exhausted, the IPA physicians may not get paid for all their services. On the other hand, if physicians provide services totaling less than the fund pool, the IPA physicians may profit.

Network or Direct-Contract Model HMOs   Network or direct-contract model HMOs contract with physicians at all levels and usually use a combination of each model type. The models contract directly with physicians to provide services to their members. A well-known example is US Healthcare of Bluebell, Pennsylvania.

Physician reimbursement may vary between capitation and discounted fee-for-service, although capitation is more common. Direct-contract models retain more of the financial risk than do the IPA models, as well as the task of managing utilization and cost controls.

According to a study by The Managed Care Information Center in Manasquan, New Jersey, HMOs are more likely to be organized as IPA-model HMOs than any other model type. The study shows that 55.5 percent of HMOs are IPAs, 18.5 percent are mixed-model HMOs, 12.3 percent are network-model HMOs, 9.0 percent are group-model HMOs, and 1.1 percent are staff-model HMOs. The remaining HMOs are mixed models.

Physician Participation and General HMO Guidelines   Physicians must apply and sign contracts to become a participating provider with HMO groups. The contract defines the patient group to be covered, the physicians' scope of services, and method of reimbursement—either discounted fee-for-service or capitation. The provider of services must file insurance claim forms, collect any deductible, co-insurance, or co-payment amounts, and write off the difference of the actual billed charge and the allowed amount.

Preferred Provider Organizations (PPOs)

A preferred provider organization (PPO) is generally defined as a group of health care providers, including physicians, hospitals, and allied institutions, that agree to provide services to a specific pool of patients. PPOs have been offered by insurance carriers, groups of physicians, and groups of hospitals.

There are generally financial incentives offered to plan holders to use the "preferred" group of "closed-panel" or member providers for care. Participants using the preferred providers will benefit from lower deductibles, co-insurance, co-payments, or other incentives. The physicians, in turn, benefit from access to new patients, increased patient utilization, and prompt fee-for-service payment from the insurer. Under PPOs, the physician's reimbursement is based on a discounted fee schedule, and payment is based on traditional fee-for-service billing.

Preferred provider organizations derive many of the cost-saving benefits from strict payment policies and discounted fee schedules. They also use some of the same techniques as HMOs to minimize utilization of services. Utilization review, second opinions, and ambulatory surgery options are often utilized to reduce costs. According to a 1993 PPO industry survey by the American Association of Preferred Provider Organizations (AAPPO):

- The number of PPOs in 1992 rose 17 percent to 681 plans from 584 plans in 1991.

- In 1992, approximately 56 million persons were enrolled in PPO plans, up from 40 million in 1991.

- Of the 681 PPOs responding, 42 percent were owned by insurance companies, 24 percent were owned by independent investors, 7 percent were owned by physician/hospital joint ventures, and another 15 percent were split between hospitals (5 percent), physicians (5 percent), and hospital alliances (15 percent).

- There were an estimated 2,700 separate PPO networks of physicians and hospitals operating throughout the United States and its territories in 1992, up more than 100 percent from 1991.

- The development of specialty PPOs covering workers' compensation increased from 20 million workers to more than 38 million workers in 1992, nearly doubling in size in a single year.

The growth of PPO enrollment and the evolution of hybrid PPO plans will continue to increase in the coming years. Practices need to review each contract presented to them and be aware of the plan's discounted fee schedule, contract requirements, and potential risk incurred by the physician. As each PPO plan varies in coverage and benefit packages, the office staff needs to be aware of all PPO plans they participate in and their policies and procedures that must be maintained for successful claim submission. One problem to be wary of when managing PPO discounts is what is referred to as a "silent PPO discount." This has become a very prevalent problem and can cost practices tens of thousands of dollars in due reimbursement that is improperly written off. Some insurance plans for which the practice does not have a signed contract with will indicate on their explanation of benefits (EOB) that they are taking their "contractual PPO discount." This is because they are part of a PPO that the practice has a signed contact with, but the plan really is not a part of the PPO network. Apparently traditional insurance plans can buy the fee schedules and physician listings of contracted providers from other insurance plans for which the practice does have a PPO contract. They use the data to reduce their payments and convince the practice staff that they must accept the "contractual PPO discount." Awareness of network health plans and PPO fee schedule amounts are critical for defeating this problem.

Point of Service Plans (POSs)

Several Blue Cross/Blue Shield plans have developed a new form of managed care that combines aspects of both PPOs and HMOs. This plan is called a point of service plan (POS). Beneficiaries may select physicians and other health care providers who are members of the POS or they may select providers outside of the POS. Financial incentives, usually in the form of lower fees, are offered to subscribers to encourage them to use member providers.

Self-funded Plans

An increasing number of large corporations are dropping traditional health insurance from commercial carriers and insuring their employees through self-funded plans. To institute a self-funded plan, the corporation usually obtains an excess liability rider (re-insurance, stop-loss coverage) and then establishes a reserve fund to pay employee medical bills.

Self-funded plans are frequently managed by a third-party administrator (TPA) that establishes a PPO or similar type of arrangement with physicians, hospitals, and other health care providers. Incentives are provided to employees to seek care from providers who have contracted with the corporation through the TPA to provide services at a discounted rate. These incentives may be in the form of first dollar coverage or bonuses to employees who do not utilize health care services unnecessarily.

Provider-Sponsored Organizations (PSOs)

A provider-sponsored organization (PSO) is a Medicare + Choice organization that is a public or private entity and is organized and operated by a health care provider or group of affiliated health care providers. Recent legislation in the Balanced Budget Act of 1997 now legally defines PSOs as a public or private entity of affiliated providers, who provide a substantial portion (60 percent for rural PSOs, 70 percent for urban PSOs) of the care. They take a substantial portion of the risk to do this on the budget (capitation) the government provides for Medicare patients. The reserve needed by a PSO is less than that required for an HMO. The shortfall in reserves is usually covered by the state. PSOs can be formed by many types of entities, such as physician-hospital organizations (PHOs), which are an affiliate organization formed by physicians and hospitals that serve as collaborative providers.

It is anticipated by the Congressional Budget Office that 10 million people eligible by Medicare will be in PSOs over the next four years, compared with just under 5 million in HMOs after nearly 12 years of marketing. HCFA estimates that HMO membership will grow from 15 percent to 18 percent over the same period that PSOs grow to serve more than 25 percent of the Medicare-eligible population.

Workers' Compensation

This is a state-required insurance plan in which employers make premium payments to a general fund. Premiums depend on the type of work performed, the duration the insurance has been in place, and the number of claims. Workers' compensation plans provide benefits in cases where an employee becomes ill or is injured as a result of his or her job. The amount of insurance an employer must carry depends on the risk of employee job-related injuries. Laws regulating workers' compensation programs vary from state to state.

When an employee is injured on the job, the employee either must go to a designated physician or can select his or her own physician for an independent medical exam (IME). The physician conducting the IME is paid a predefined amount. When treating a patient covered under a workers' compensation program, be sure to obtain a "Statement of Injury" form from the patient's employer. In addition, some programs require special "medical report" forms to be completed for claim adjudication.

Workers' compensation cases are handled by the commercial insurance carrier chosen by the employer. Before admission, the carrier should be notified and verification of coverage obtained. The *patient should have a written authorization form* (possibly in the form of an incident report) signed by a representative of the employer. If not, this documentation should be requested of the employer. It should be established with the employer whether or not it recognizes responsibility for the injury. If so, a letter stating this obligation should be requested.

If a workers' compensation case is denied by the carrier, the patient has the right to appeal the denial to the state board and request a hearing. As long as the patient has an appeal pending, even though the claim may be previously denied, neither the hospital nor the physician can pursue payment from the patient. Inquiry regarding case status can be done either through the carrier or through the state board of workers' compensation. Additional forms and filing requirements may vary from state to state.

In the next chapter, we will cover the various coding systems used to report services rendered by physicians.

3 The Coding Systems

Objectives

After completing this chapter, you should be able to:

- Identify the three volumes of *International Classification of Diseases–Ninth Revision, Clinical Modification* (ICD-9-CM), as they pertain to medical practices

- Recognize the general ICD-9-CM coding guidelines

- Identify specific coding symbols, abbreviations, and notations

- Understand the purpose of fourth and fifth digits

- Understand the difference between V and E codes and the difference between Includes and Excludes Notes

- Locate the Neoplasm and Hypertension Tables in the index

- Understand what the term *cross-reference* means

- Describe how the three levels of HCPCS differ

- Recognize the HCPCS coding guidelines and understand how CPT is organized

- Recognize the format of CPT and CPT coding guidelines

- Define Evaluation and Management Services

- Understand the rules that apply to surgery coding

- Understand how CPT modifiers are used

Introduction

Practices use coding systems to communicate the procedures and services provided to patients and the reasons they were provided. Physician practices benefit from learning how to properly use the coding systems in two ways. First, appropriate use of codes helps ensure proper payment from third-party payers and patients. Payers may reject or delay payment on claims without codes or with codes used incorrectly. Proper coding can enhance a practice's relationship with patients. When claims are coded accurately, patients who file their own claims will have fewer problems obtaining payment from their insurance company.

Second, appropriate use of codes reduces a practice's audit liability. When the reported codes do not accurately describe the procedures and services rendered, the physician may be accused of fraudulent billing, that is, billing for services and procedures other than those provided. Thus, learning how to code accurately and properly is in the practice's best interest.

Three coding systems are currently used in the United States. Each system is unique and serves a specific purpose in communicating to third-party payers what the physician did and why the physician did it. First we give a brief overview of each system. The following sections give detailed information about each system.

1. *Current Procedural Terminology (CPT)™, Fourth Edition.* Created and maintained by the American Medical Association, CPT consists of more than 7,000 codes used to report procedures and services. CPT codes communicate to third-party payers what the physician did. CPT codes are five-digit numbers accompanied by narrative descriptions. A two- or five-digit numeric modifier may also be used for additional modification of the CPT code description. All third-party payers accept CPT codes.

2. HCFA's Common Procedure Coding System (HCPCS). HCPCS (pronounced "hick-picks") was created by the Health Care Financing Administration (HCFA). HCPCS is a three-level coding system. Level I is the CPT code. Level II is a national alphanumeric code that begins with a letter followed by four numbers. Level II codes are usually thought of as the codes used to report supplies and injections to Medicare and other payers. Level III is a state alphanumeric code.

3. *International Classification of Diseases–Ninth Revision–Clinical Modification* (ICD-9-CM). This coding system is used to report patient illnesses, injuries, complaints, and/or symptoms, referred to as diagnoses. ICD-9-CM communicates to third-party payers the need for medical services, or why the physician performed the service. Like CPT, the ICD-9-CM system consists of code numbers and narrative descriptions. However, ICD-9-CM codes may range from three to five digits, depending on the level of specificity defined. The physician (or coder) should code to the highest level of specificity. All ICD-9-CM codes are numeric except for E and V codes.

CPT™

CPT is the coding system used to describe services and procedures provided by physicians. Produced, published, and maintained by the American Medical Association, it is updated annually. A new publication is released each November, and the codes become effective on January 1. Physicians should purchase the new CPT volume each year to ensure their use of the most current codes. The submission of deleted or incorrect CPT codes may result in reimbursement delay or denial or audit liability. Copies of the CPT book are available from the American Medical Association.

CPT Organization

Codes in CPT are organized in six logical sections according to the types of services or procedures provided. These sections begin with guidelines that provide important coding rules and other information. It is important to be familiar with the six sections of CPT and the code number ranges in each section in order to better understand where to locate codes for different procedures or services. The six sections of CPT and their associated code ranges are as follows:

1. Evaluation and Management Services (codes **99201–99499**).
   Physicians use codes from this section to report office, hospital, consultative, nursing home, and other related "visit" services. The book starts with this series of codes because they are the most frequently reported services by physicians.

2. Anesthesia (codes **00100–01999**).
   The codes in this section describe anesthesia services any physician can use.

3. Surgery (codes **10040–69979**).
   Surgery is the longest section in CPT. It includes codes that describe procedures ranging from simple wound repairs to organ transplants.

4. Radiology (codes **70010–79999**).
   Diagnostic radiology, diagnostic ultrasound, radiation oncology, and nuclear medicine are covered in this section of codes.

5. Pathology and Laboratory (codes **80002–89399**).
   These codes describe laboratory tests and pathology services.

6. Medicine (codes **90701–99199**).
   This last section provides codes that describe a wide variety of medical services ranging from immunizations to electrocardiograms to psychotherapy.

CPT also provides information about the proper use and selection of codes. Specifically, you will find:

Introductions (roman numeral page numbers). These contain explanations of and instructions for the use of CPT.

Guidelines. Guidelines, which precede each section of CPT, contain important information specific to the section, including a discussion of applicable modifiers.

Appendices. Six appendices follow the Medicine section. Appendix A provides a complete list of CPT's two-digit numeric modifiers and their descriptions. Appendix B summarizes code additions, deletions, and changes that occur for that year in the volume. Appendix C lists the short descriptions (28 characters or less) for each of the new, changed, or deleted codes. Appendices B and C are helpful to practices that use a computer to generate claims, as they provide a quick reference for updating the code databases. Appendix D contains clinical examples of the Evaluation and Management Services and their corresponding CPT codes. Appendix E contains a summary of CPT add-on codes. Appendix F contains a summary of CPT codes exempt from modifier '-51.'

Index. The index follows Appendix F. Use it to locate the correct CPT code for a procedure. *Never* code directly from the index, as that can lead to coding errors. The index often lists a range of codes or multiple codes from which to choose. Read the complete descriptions, notes or parenthetic phrases, and guidelines of each code to ensure you select the correct one.

CPT Format

The CPT coding system utilizes an indented format, like that shown in the following example. This format is used to save space. You must be careful when reporting indented codes because the indented portion refers back to a common portion of the code above, which is not indented. The common portion is the portion printed *before the semicolon* (;). For example,

"Laryngoscopy, flexible fiberoptic;"

is common to codes 31575 through 31579. Thus, code 31576 is used to report:

"Laryngoscopy, flexible fiberoptic; with biopsy"

Following is an example of the indented format.

17106	Destruction of cutaneous vascular proliferative lesions (eg, laser technique); less than 10 sq cm
17107	10.0–50.0 sq cm
17108	over 50.0 sq cm
•17110*	Destruction by any method of flat warts, molluscum contagiosum, or milia; up to 14 lesions
17111	15 or more lesions
17250*	Chemical cauterization of granulation tissue (proud flesh, sinus, or fistula) (17250 is not to be used with removal or excision codes for the same lesion)

In addition to the indented format, the Surgery section uses a consistent "universal" format that, like a road map, helps you locate codes. Surgery codes are first arranged by body system, such as integumentary, musculoskeletal, respiratory, and so on. As appropriate, codes within a body system are then arranged from the top of the system to the bottom, or from the outside to the inside of the body. Codes are further organized into types of procedures, such as incision, excision, repair, and the like.

CPT Symbols

CPT uses various symbols. These symbols and their meanings are described below.

- The solid circle (or bullet) appears to the left of codes new to CPT. "New" means the codes were not listed in the previous year's publication.

▲ A solid triangle (or delta) to the left of a code signifies that the code's narrative description has changed since last year's book. Description changes may be significant or relatively minor.

✱ Stars appear to the right of several code numbers in the Surgery section of CPT. The star signifies that because of the indefinite preoperative and postoperative services, the usual "package" concept for surgical services cannot be applied.

►◄ The two triangles facing each other are used to indicate new and revised text other than the procedure descriptors.

➲ The arrow signifies that in the Professional Edition of CPT the code can be referenced to the CPT Assistant.

✚ The plus sign signifies "add-on codes"—some precedents are carried out in addition to the primary procedure performed. All add-on codes are exempt from the multiple procedure concept.

⊘ This symbol indicates codes that are exempt from the use of modifier -51, but have not been designated as CPT add-on procedures/services.

The circle and triangle symbols are useful when referring to a specific code, because they identify the changes in each new volume of CPT. Symbols are a quick reference, saving the practice time from referring to Appendix B for each code it wishes to report.

CPT Notes

CPT contains several hundred notes and parenthetical remarks designed to assist with code selection. Notes precede groups of codes, follow a code(s) to which they apply, and, in at least one case, follow a section of codes. Parenthetical notes and remarks are typically provided to refer the coder to related procedures, or, in the case of deleted codes, to refer to codes that replace the deleted ones.

To code properly, review all notes pertaining to the code you are considering. Failure to read and understand notes can result in lower insurance reimbursements and audit liability.

CPT Index

The CPT index is an excellent starting point for locating codes. The page preceding the index gives instructions on how to use the index. Most codes can be located by looking under:

1. The name of the procedure or service (for example, incision, endoscopy)

2. The organ system or body area (for example, lung, genitourinary)

3. The patient's condition (for example, dislocation, pregnancy)

4. The use of synonyms (for example, renal for kidney), eponyms (for example, Abbe-Estlander), or abbreviations (for example, ECG, CAT scan)

Subterms, which follow most of the main terms in CPT, should be reviewed carefully as they may affect code assignments.

CPT Coding Guidelines

This section presents basic coding rules and special requirements that apply to frequently used sections of CPT.

General Rules   The CPT coding process involves six basic steps that, when followed, increase the likelihood of accurate code selection.

1. Identify the procedures and services provided. This entails reviewing the patient's record, operative report, radiology, laboratory reports, and so on. The first step in proper coding is identifying the procedures and services provided during the physician-patient encounter. Identification of routine services, such as office visits, is fairly straightforward. Identification of multiple services or complex procedures (especially surgeries) requires a higher-level understanding of CPT and of billing rules.

2. Consult the index to locate the code numbers. You must determine the main term for each procedure to be coded and then identify that main term in the alphabetic index. Note any listed subterms below the main term and refer to cross-references provided in the index.

3. Locate the code(s) in the main body of the CPT book. Always refer to the code in the main body of the book, which may include notes or other important information that may affect code selection. Never code directly from the index.

4. Review the notes and parenthetical remarks associated with the codes. Notes and parenthetical remarks associated with the codes may contain special rules or information that may affect your code selection. Also review the guidelines at the beginning of the section and subsection notes when included.

5. Code the billable procedures and services. After specific procedures and services have been identified, the next step is to code them.

6. Modify as necessary. Some situations will require adding appropriate modifiers to codes. Modifiers are discussed later in this chapter.

Note: Compare the final code description with the procedure or service provided to ensure that all components have been reported.

Evaluation and Management Services   Nearly one third of all services rendered by physicians are reported using codes from this section of CPT. Therefore, you must pay special attention to the rules related to coding evaluation and management (E/M) services. Rules for coding these services are in the E/M guidelines beginning on page 1 of the CPT book.

E/M services are coded according to the *content* of the service provided. The extent of the history taken by the physician, the extent of the examination, and the complexity of medical decision making involved are defined as *key components*. Four levels of history, four levels of examination, and four levels of decision making are defined. In most cases, code selection will depend on matching the levels of each key component provided with the levels specified in the codes. The four levels are problem focused, expanded problem focused, detailed, and comprehensive. These four clinical levels determine the numeric billing level that is forwarded to the carrier.

For example, if the physician saw an established patient in the office, took an expanded problem-focused history, performed an expanded problem-focused examination, and determined that medical decision making was of low complexity, code **99213** would be selected.

99213 Office or other outpatient visit for the evaluation and management of an established patient, which requires at least two of these three key components:

- an expanded problem-focused history;

- an expanded problem-focused examination;

- medical decision-making of low complexity.

Counseling and coordination of care with other providers or agencies are provided consistent with the nature of the problem(s) and the patient's and/or family's needs.

Usually, the presenting problems(s) are of low to moderate severity. Physicians typically spend 15 minutes face-to-face with the patient and/or family.

When a new patient is evaluated, all three key components are used for establishing the numeric level of billing. The lowest of the three levels of key components is used. When an established patient is evaluated, only two of three key components are used for billing purposes. The lowest of the two levels determines the numeric level of billing.

Code selection for E/M services can be affected by other factors, called *contributing factors*. These include the nature of the patient's presenting problem(s), the provision of counseling and/or coordination of care services, and the amount of time the physician spends with the patient. While these factors are not key to choosing the E/M code, they can affect selection.

According to CPT E/M guidelines, time may become the controlling factor in selecting E/M codes only when more than 50 percent of the service rendered to the patient was related to counseling and/or coordination of care. Understanding how "time" is defined is important when time is used as the controlling factor in billing. For office E/M services, time is defined as time spent face-to-face with the patient; for hospital E/M services, time is defined as time spent on the patient's floor or unit.

It is important that all Medicare updates from local carriers be read, as coding guidelines and documentation requirements change frequently.

E/M Documentation Guidelines   HCFA's revised documentation guidelines for E/M services have been indefinitely delayed. At this time, the 1994 or 1997 guidelines may be used, whichever is most advantageous to the provider. It is estimated that implementation of the future guidelines would be conceivable by July 1999 or later.

Surgery Coding   Special rules apply to the coding of surgical procedures. Three of the most important rules are discussed below.

Surgical Package Rules. Beginning coders often ask what services are included with surgical procedures. To address this issue, the CPT system provides the "surgical package" (or global surgery) definition. Shown in the Surgery section guidelines, it specifies components assumed to be included in the surgery charge. The components are:

- The operation itself

- Local and topical anesthetics (if provided)

- Digital blocks (if provided)

- The normal, uncomplicated follow-up care related to the procedure

Thus, the physician should not bill separately for local or topical anesthetics, digital blocks, or hospital or office visits that are part of the normal follow-up. If the patient develops complications during follow-up, treatment of the complications may be coded. Preoperative services such as consultations, office visits, and initial hospital care are often billed separately by physicians. Payment of these services will depend on third-party payment policy.

The Medicare definition of the surgical package delineates the number of preoperative and postoperative days included as well as the types of services included in the package.

The Medicare global surgery package includes:

- A one-day preoperative period. This includes all preoperative visits by the surgeon in or out of the hospital beginning the day before surgery

- Intraoperative services that are a part of the procedure

- A standard 90-day postoperative period (or follow-up) including any services the surgeon provided during that time, unless service was due to an unrelated condition. Minor surgical procedures include a zero to ten-day postoperative period. There is no postoperative period for endoscopic diagnostic procedures performed through an existing body orifice

All medically necessary return trips to the operating room can be billed separately and will be paid at a reduced rate.

Several other payers also have surgical package definitions that may differ from the ones listed above. Physicians and staff need to be aware of the differences and code accordingly. Check with your local carriers for clarification of their policies.

Note: The global surgical package is very important in physician office claim submission. However, the surgical package is *not* applicable to hospital coding for the facility fee.

Separate Procedures. CPT codes were designed to combine several procedures that were often performed together, so reporting would use a minimum number of codes but still provide a complete picture of the service provided. In some cases, CPT has identified certain procedures as "separate procedures," which means these can be coded separately when performed independently and not in conjunction with the major or primary procedure.

Example:

52601   Transurethral electrosurgical resection of the prostate, including control of postoperative bleeding, complete (vasectomy, meatotomy, cystourethroscopy, urethral calibration and/or dilation, and internal urethrotomy are included)

55250   Vasectomy, unilateral or bilateral (separate procedure), including postoperative semen examination(s)

In the above example, a transurethral resection of the prostate and a vasectomy were performed. Following the separate procedure guidelines, only code **52601** should be assigned because it incorporates both the resection of the prostate and the vasectomy. Code **55250** is identified as a separate procedure and can be reported separately when only the vasectomy is performed.

Starred Procedure Rules. A star appears to the right of several code numbers in the Surgery section of CPT. The star signifies that the surgical package defined above does not apply to these codes and that special coding rules should be followed instead. Note that starred procedures are invariably minor surgeries that may or may not have associated preoperative and/or postoperative services. Thus, the surgical package does not logically apply. This means that, subject to the rules for coding starred procedures in the surgery section guidelines, preoperative and postoperative care can be billed separately from the procedure.

CPT Modifiers

CPT contains two-digit numeric modifiers that are used to report situations in which the service or procedure was altered by some specific circumstance. In such situations, the circumstance does not affect the selection of the CPT code. For example, the physician performs a bilateral tympanostomy under general anesthesia.

Because code 69436 is a unilateral procedure code, the modifier -50 must be assigned to identify this procedure as bilateral, as shown in the example below:

69436-50   Tympanostomy (requiring insertion of ventilating tube), general anesthesia

The addition of the modifier indicates that the physician performed the procedure bilaterally.

All modifiers are listed in CPT's Appendix A. Modifiers relevant to each of the six sections of CPT are also provided in the section guidelines. Although CPT provides both two-digit (for example, '-51') and five-digit (for example, 09951) modifiers, most payers accept, if not require, two-digit modifiers. Certain modifiers have specific uses (for example, '-21', '-24', '-25' with E/M services). Some modifiers are commonly used with certain types of codes (for example, surgery, medicine), so as not to preclude or restrict their use to only one specialty. Use the modifier that depicts the circumstance most accurately.

Modifiers and Descriptors

-21 or 09921   **Prolonged Evaluation and Management Services:** This modifier is appropriate for use when service provided is prolonged and more than is usually required for the highest level of E/M service within a category. Appropriate documentation should also be sent with the claim to support the use of the modifier and the increase of payment requested.

This modifier should be used for E/M services code(s).

-22 or 09922   **Unusual Procedural Services:** This modifier is appropriate when the service provided is greater than that usually required. A special report may be required to describe the unusual service provided.

This modifier is commonly used with anesthesia, surgery, radiology, and pathology/ laboratory procedure code(s).

-23 or 09923   **Unusual Anesthesia:** When a procedure that usually requires local or no anesthetic must be performed under a general anesthetic because of unusual circumstances, modifier -23 should be reported along with the procedure code.

This modifier should be used for anesthesia code(s).

-24 or 09924   **Unrelated Evaluation and Management Service by the Same Physician During a Postoperative Period:** This modifier is appropriate to describe an E/M service provided to a patient during the postoperative period that is unrelated to the original procedure.

This modifier should be used for E/M services code(s).

-25 or 09925   **Significant, Separately Identifiable Evaluation and Management Service by the Same Physician on the Same Day of the Procedure or Other Service:** This modifier is appropriate to use when the physician needs to indicate, on the day a procedure or service identified by a CPT code was performed, that the patient's condition required a significant, separately identifiable E/M service above and beyond the other service provided or beyond the usual preoperative and postoperative care associated with the procedure. The E/M service may be prompted by the symptom or condition for which the procedure and/or service was provided. Different diagnoses are not required for reporting of the E/M services on the same date.

This modifier should be used for E/M services code(s).

-26 or 09926   **Professional Component:** The majority of the procedures included in CPT include both the technical and professional component. This modifier is used to indicate that the physician provided only the professional component, not the technical.

This modifier is commonly used with surgery, radiology, medicine, and pathology/laboratory procedure code(s).

-32 or 09932   **Mandated Services:** Mandated services refers to a confirmatory opinion conducted at the request of the payer.

This modifier is commonly used with E/M services, anesthesia, surgery, radiology, pathology/laboratory, and medicine procedure code(s).

-47 or 09947   **Anesthesia by Surgeon:** When the physician administers anesthesia in addition to performing the surgery, this modifier is reported.

This modifier should be used with surgery procedure code(s).

-50 or 09950 **Bilateral Procedure:** There are only a few codes in CPT that distinguish between unilateral and bilateral procedures. This modifier is appropriate for use to describe a bilateral procedure. There are several ways to report the bilateral modifier. Coders should check with individual insurance carriers to determine their preference.

This modifier should be used with surgery procedure code(s).

-51 or 09951 **Multiple Procedures:** When more than one procedure is performed on the same day during the same surgical episode, this modifier may be assigned. The first code listed should be the most resource intensive or the highest paying. Medicare reimbursement is reduced by 50 percent for the second procedure, 25 percent for the third procedure, etc.

This modifier is most commonly used with anesthesia, surgery, and radiology procedure code(s).

-52 or 09952 **Reduced Services:** When the service documented in the medical record is less in time or effort than the descriptor in the CPT manual, this modifier may be reported to indicate that a lower level of service was provided. In addition, the charge should be decreased. **Note:** For hospital outpatient reporting of a previously scheduled procedure/service that is reduced or canceled as a result of extenuating circumstances or those that threaten the well-being of the patient before or after administration of anesthesia, see modifiers -73 and -74.

This modifier is commonly used with E/M services, surgery, radiology, and pathology/ laboratory procedure code(s).

-53 or 09953 **Discontinued Procedure:** This modifier is used when the physician elects to terminate a surgical or diagnostic procedure because of extenuating circumstances or those that threaten the well-being of the patient. **Note:** This modifier is not used to report the elective cancellation of a procedure before the patient's anesthesia induction and/or surgical preparation in the operating suite. For outpatient hospital/ambulatory surgery center reporting of a previously scheduled procedure/service that is reduced or canceled as a result of extenuating circumstances or those that threaten the well-being of the patient before or after administration of anesthesia, see modifiers -73 and -74.

This modifier is commonly used with anesthesia, surgery, radiology, and pathology/laboratory procedure code(s).

-54 or 09954 **Surgical Care Only:** As mentioned earlier, the surgical package includes the procedure and normal preoperative and postoperative care (excluding starred procedures). In some cases, however, the physician may perform only the surgical procedure. In these cases, modifier -54 or 09954 should be reported. In addition, the charges related to that code should be reduced.

This modifier should be used with surgery procedure code(s).

-55 or 09955 **Postoperative Management Only:** When the physician provides only the postoperative management (not the preoperative or operative service) for a patient, modifier -55 or 09955 is reported. Again, the charges related to that code should be reduced to reflect the postoperative management fees only.

This modifier should be used with surgery procedure code(s).

-56 or 09956 **Preoperative Management Only:** When the physician provides only the preoperative management (not the operative and postoperative service) for a patient, modifier -56 or 09956 is reported. Again, the charges related to that code should be reduced to reflect the preoperative management fees only.

This modifier should be used with surgery procedure code(s).

-57 or 09957 **Decision for Surgery:** An evaluation and management service that resulted in the initial decision to perform the surgery may be identified by adding the modifier -57 to the appropriate level of E/M service, or the separate five-digit modifier 09957 may be used.

This modifier should be used with E/M services code(s).

-58 or 09958 **Staged or Related Procedure or Service by the Same Physician During the Postoperative Period:** The physician may need to indicate that the performance of a procedure or service during the postoperative period was (1) planned prospectively at the time of the original procedure (staged); (2) more extensive than the original procedure; or (3) for therapy after a diagnostic surgical procedure. This circumstance may be reported by adding the modifier -58 to the staged or related procedure, or the separate five-digit modifier 09958 may be used. **Note:** This modifier is not used to report the treatment of a problem that requires a return to the operating room.

This modifier is commonly used with surgery, radiology, and medicine procedure code(s).

-59 or 09959   **Distinct Procedural Service:** Under certain circumstances, the physician may need to indicate that a procedure or service was distinct or independent from other services performed on the same day. This may represent a different session or patient encounter, different procedure or surgery, different site or organ system, separate incision/excision, separate lesion, or separate injury (or area of injury in extensive injuries) not ordinarily performed on the same day by the same physician. However, when another already established modifier is appropriate, it should be used instead of modifier -59. Only if no more descriptive modifier is available, and the use of modifier -59 best explains the circumstances, should modifier -59 be used.

This modifier is commonly used with anesthesia, surgery, radiology, pathology/laboratory, and medicine procedure code(s).

-62 or 09962   **Two Surgeons (Co-surgery):** Although most surgical procedures are performed by one surgeon, there are some difficult surgeries requiring two surgeons. When two surgeons work together as primary surgeons performing distinct part(s) of a single reportable procedure, each surgeon should report his/her distinct operative work by adding the modifier -62 to the single definitive procedure code. Each surgeon should report the co-surgery once using the same procedure code. If additional procedure(s) (including add-on procedures) are performed during the same operative session, separate code(s) may be reported without the modifier -62 added. Modifier code 09962 may be used as an alternative to modifier -62. **Note:** If a co-surgeon acts as an assistant in the performance of additional procedure(s) during the same surgical session, those services may be reported using separate procedure code(s) with the modifier -80 or modifier -81 added, as appropriate.

This modifier is commonly used with surgery and radiology procedure code(s).

-66 or 09966   **Surgical Team:** Complex surgical procedures, such as heart and renal transplants, require a highly trained team of physicians and support staff to successfully conduct the procedure. Modifier -66 or 09966 should be reported, indicating to the insurance carrier that more than one physician will be submitting claims for reimbursement.

This modifier is commonly used with surgery and radiology procedure code(s).

-73 or 09973   **Discontinued Outpatient Hospital/Ambulatory Surgery Center (ASC) Procedure Prior to the Administration of Anesthesia:** Due to extenuating circumstances or those that threaten the well-being of the patient, the physician may cancel a surgical or diagnostic procedure subsequent to the patient's surgical preparation (including sedation when provided, and being taken to the room where the procedure is to be performed), but prior to the administration of anesthesia (local, regional block[s], or general). Modifier -73 or 09973 can be added to the procedure code for the intended service that is prepared for but canceled. **Note:** The elective cancellation of a service before the administration of anesthesia and/or surgical preparation of the patient should not be reported.

-74 or 09974   **Discontinued Outpatient Hospital/Ambulatory Surgery Center (ASC) Procedure After Administration of Anesthesia:** Due to extenuating circumstances or those that threaten the well-being of the patient, the physician may terminate a surgical or diagnostic procedure after the administration of anesthesia (local, regional block[s], or general) or after the procedure was started (incision made, intubation started, scope inserted, etc.). Modifier -74 or 09974 can be added to the procedure code when the procedure was started but terminated. **Note:** The elective cancellation of a service before the administration of anesthesia and/or surgical preparation of the patient should not be reported.

-76 or 09976 **Repeat Procedure by Same Physician:** Situations will exist where a procedure will need to be repeated by the same physician because of problems with the patient, equipment, emergencies, complications etc. The repeat procedure is to be performed subsequent to the original procedure or service. In these situations, modifier -76 or 09976 should be reported. Documentation should include quite clearly why the surgery was repeated.

This modifier is commonly used with surgery, radiology, pathology/laboratory, and medicine procedure code(s).

-77 or 09977 **Repeat Procedure by Another Physician:** This modifier is similar to the previous modifier except that the physician performing the repeat surgery is not the same. As with the previous modifier, repeat procedures may be required because of problems with the patient, equipment, emergencies, complications, etc. The repeat procedure is to be performed during the same day as the original surgery. For instance, a physician may perform a percutaneous transluminal coronary angioplasty (PTCA) for a patient with acute coronary occlusion. Later in the day, the occlusion redevelops. If the original physician was not available to perform the PTCA, another physician may perform it. The second physician would report the PTCA code, as well as this modifier to alert the insurance carrier that the procedure was indeed performed two times in one day. Again, documentation should clearly state why the surgery was repeated and that a different physician conducted the second procedure.

This modifier is commonly used with surgery, radiology, and medicine procedure code(s).

-78 or 09978 **Return to the Operating Room for a Related Procedure During the Postoperative Period:** In some cases, a physician will be required to return to the operating room during the postoperative period of a procedure to address a condition that is related to the initial procedure. To report these situations, modifier -78 or 09978 should be assigned along with the procedure code. For instance, a patient having undergone abdominal surgery returns to the operating room ten days after surgery for repair of abdominal wound dehiscence. The wound dehiscence repair, which is related to the original procedure, occurs during the postoperative period of that first procedure. Therefore, modifier -78 or 09978 should be reported along with the wound dehiscence repair code. Documentation in the medical record should clearly indicate the reason for the return visit to the operating room.

This modifier is commonly used with surgery, radiology, and medicine procedure code(s).

-79 or 09979   **Unrelated Procedure or Service by the Same Physician During the Postoperative Period:** In other cases, a problem will arise requiring surgery or service by a physician who has recently performed surgery on the patient. If this service or second surgery is provided during the postoperative period of the first surgery, modifier -79 or 09979 is reported to explain the additional procedure or service. For instance, a patient may have had a cholecystectomy and is still in the postoperative period of that surgery and now is admitted to the hospital with multiple lacerations and contusions secondary to an automobile accident. Modifier -79 is applicable to describe the reason for the second admission while still in the postoperative period of the first procedure. Again, documentation should clearly include the diagnoses and services/procedures provided.

This modifier is commonly used with surgery, radiology, and medicine procedure code(s).

-80 or 09980   **Assistant Surgeon:** When an assistant surgeon is required to help in performing a surgical procedure, the assisting surgeon should report modifier -80 or 09980 along with the appropriate surgery code. It is imperative that the assisting surgeon and primary surgeon submit the same code to the insurance carriers (with the assisting surgeon using modifier -80). Coders should note that the primary surgeon does not have to report modifier -80. The operative report should clearly state the reason for having an assistant surgeon, as well as his/her contribution to the surgery.

This modifier should be used with surgery and radiology procedure code(s).

-81 or 09981   **Minimum Assistant Surgeon:** There may be a situation in which a physician requires some assistance in the operating room because of a minor problem encountered during the procedure. In these cases, modifier -81 or 09981 is reported to indicate that "minimum assistance" was provided. As with the previous modifier, the assisting surgeon reports the modifier along with the surgery code. Again, the surgery code submitted by the primary surgeon should be the same as the surgery code submitted by the assisting surgeon. Documentation in the record should provide the reason for requiring the minimum assistance.

This modifier should be used with surgery procedure code(s).

-82 or 09982   **Assistant Surgeon (when qualified resident surgeon not available):** In most teaching hospitals, residents are available to serve as assistant surgeon when the procedure requires an assistant. In these situations, if a resident is not available and another nonresident surgeon assists, modifier -82 is reported along with the surgery code by the assisting surgeon. The surgery code submitted by the assistant and the primary surgeon should be the same. Again, documentation in the record should indicate the fact that a qualified resident was not available and that an assistant was required for the procedure performed.

This modifier should be used with surgery procedure code(s).

-90 or 09990   **Reference (Outside) Laboratory:** When the physician reports a procedure that was not done by his or her facility or office, this modifier should be assigned.

This modifier is commonly used with surgery, radiology, and pathology/laboratory procedure code(s).

-99 or 09999   **Multiple Modifiers:** When more than one modifier is appropriate to report the services provided to the patient, this modifier may be assigned to identify the use of multiple modifiers. The CPT code should be reported with modifier -99 with the other modifiers listed as part of the description of the service or as follows:

EXAMPLE:	23931-99	Incision and drainage, upper arm or elbow area; infected bursa
	00947	Anesthesia provided by the surgeon
	00950	Bilateral procedure

This modifier is commonly used with surgery, radiology, and medicine procedure code(s).

HCPCS

HCPCS (pronounced hick-picks, not hix-picks) is an abbreviation for the federal government's three-level coding system—the Health Care Financing Administration (HCFA) Common Procedure Coding System.

HCFA is the federal agency that administers the Medicare and Medicaid programs. In the 1980s, with the increasing use of electronic claims, the HCFA recognized the need for a nationwide standardized coding system. Because Medicare and Medicaid pay for physicians' services as well as other medical services and supplies, the HCFA developed the following three levels of codes.

CPT 1999 includes all Level I and Level II modifiers approved for physician and hospital outpatient use.

Level I—CPT

The American Medical Association (AMA) developed and published CPT in 1966. It is used to report the procedures and services of physicians and services provided under the supervision of physicians, such as physical therapy. The Current Procedural Terminology manual, abbreviated CPT, expanded to a five-digit system. In agreement with the AMA, HCFA adopted CPT as the first level of HCPCS coding. CPT, copyrighted by the AMA, includes more than 7,000 numeric codes. CPT represents between 85 percent and 90 percent of HCPCS.

Level II—National Codes

Level II codes are for services and supplies not found in CPT, such as oral and injectable medications; durable medical equipment; prosthetics; orthotics; medical and surgical supplies; ambulance services, chiropractic, dental, and certain vision services and supplies; and temporary codes developed by HCFA. Level II codes are five digits. They begin with the letters A through V. As implied in the name, Level II national codes are used by all Medicare carriers (Part B) and intermediaries (Part A), and Medicaid in all states.

Level III—Local Codes

Each Medicare carrier may use, on approval of HCFA, local codes intended for use only in its state or region. These five-digit codes begin with the letters S, W, Y, and Z. Very few Level III codes remain in use because most codes needed now appear in Level I (CPT) or Level II. Level III local codes are usually issued each year in a bulletin or newsletter by the Medicare carrier for the state or region.

Modifiers Approved for Hospital Outpatient Use

Level I (CPT) Modifiers

-50   Bilateral Procedure

-52   Reduced Services

-59   Distinct Procedural Service

-73   Discontinued Outpatient Procedure Prior to Anesthesia Administration

-74   Discontinued Outpatient Procedure After Anesthesia Administration

-76   Repeat Procedure by Same Physician

-77   Repeat Procedure by Another Physician

Level II (HCPCS/National) Modifiers

-LT   Left side (used to identify procedures performed on the left side of the body)

-RT   Right side (used to identify procedures performed on the right side of the body)

-E1   Upper left, eyelid

-E2   Lower left, eyelid

-E3   Upper right, eyelid

-E4   Lower right, eyelid

-FA   Left hand, thumb

-F1   Left hand, second digit

-F2   Left hand, third digit

-F3   Left hand, fourth digit

-F4   Left hand, fifth digit

-F5   Right hand, thumb

-F6   Right hand, second digit

-F7   Right hand, third digit

-F8   Right hand, fourth digit

-F9   Right hand, fifth digit

-LC   Left circumflex, coronary artery (Hospitals use with codes 92980-92984, 92995, 92996)

-LD   Left anterior descending coronary artery (Hospitals use with codes 92980-92984, 92995, 92996)

-RC   Right coronary artery (Hospitals use with codes 92980-92984, 92995, 92996)

-QM   Ambulance service provided under arrangement by a provider of services

-QN   Ambulance service furnished directly by a provider of services

-QR   Repeat laboratory test performed on the same day

-TA   Left foot, great toe

-T1   Left foot, second digit

-T2   Left foot, third digit

-T3   Left foot, fourth digit

-T4   Left foot, fifth digit

-T5   Right foot, great toe

-T6   Right foot, second digit

-T7   Right foot, third digit

-T8   Right foot, fourth digit

-T9   Right foot, fifth digit

HCPCS Coding Guidelines

HCPCS Level II and Level III codes are reported on claims in the same manner as Level I (CPT) codes. Medicare requires that physicians and hospitals use certain Level II codes instead of less specific CPT codes in certain circumstances. For example, covered and injectable medications must be submitted with the specific Level II code that begins with "J," as well as the CPT code from the Medicine section. The Level II codes beginning with "A" must be used for billing covered supplies, such as surgical trays. Each Medicare carrier and intermediary can provide you with billing rules for Level II and Level III codes.

Codes Accepted by Your Carriers

Table 3.1 will help you determine the codes accepted by your carriers (CPT, HCPCS National and Local, and ICD-9-CM). Defined by the type of payer, such as Blue Cross/Blue Shield or Medicaid, and by type of code, such as CPT or ICD-9-CM, the table provides an overview of standard policies of the listed types of carriers.

Table 3.1   Which Carriers Accept Which Codes

Coding System	Insurance Carriers			
	Commercial Carriers	Blue Cross/ Blue Shield	Medicare	Medicaid
CPT	Virtually all commercial carriers accept CPT codes	All BC/BS carriers accept CPT codes	All Medicare carriers accept CPT codes	All Medicaid Programs accept CPT codes or variations thereof
HCPCS National Codes	Many commercial carriers are starting to accept CPT codes	If BC/BS runs your Medicare program, they might accept HCPCS national codes	All Medicare carriers accept some HCPCS national codes (payment depends on coverage)	Most Medicaid programs accept HCPCS national codes
HCPCS Local Codes	Some commercial carriers will accept HCPCS local codes	If BC/BS runs your Medicare program, they might accept HCPCS local codes	Your Medicare carrier will accept its own HCPCS local codes	Many Medicaid programs accept HCPCS local codes
ICD-9-CM Diagnosis Codes	Virtually all commercial carriers will accept ICD-9-CM codes	All BC/BS carriers accept ICD-9-CM codes	All Medicare carriers accept ICD-9-CM codes	Virtually all Medicaid programs accept ICD-9-CM codes

Table 3.2   Codes Accepted by Your Carriers

Coding System	Insurance Carriers			
	Commercial Carriers	Blue Cross/ Blue Shield	Medicare	Medicaid
CPT				
HCPCS National Codes				
HCPCS Local Codes				
ICD-9-CM Diagnosis Codes				

You can use the blank version of Table 3.2, which follows the completed Table 3.1, to list specific carriers in your area and their acceptance policies of the different coding systems.

ICD-9-CM

The *International Classification of Diseases–Ninth Revision–Clinical Modification* (ICD-9-CM) coding system was developed in 1978 by the U.S. National Center for Health Statistics as a statistical classification system. It was created to replace the ICD-A system and to allow for better reporting of both inpatient and outpatient conditions. The ICD-A system, and now the ICD-9 system, were developed by the World Health Organization in Switzerland. The U.S. National Center for Health Statistics added the "clinical modification" (CM) so that the ICD-9 system could be used for insurance reimbursement in the United States. ICD-9-CM is used by virtually all third-party payers as the coding system for describing patient conditions. It is updated annually in October. Physicians should use the most current ICD-9-CM coding books to ensure correct code assignment. It is expected that the next revision of ICD (ICD-10) will not be used by payers until sometime after the year 2000.

The purpose of ICD-9-CM coding is threefold:

- To establish the medical necessity for the visit or service
- To provide statistics for morbidity and mortality rates
- To take the written description of a disease or state and translate that information into numbers, producing a common language

The complete ICD-9-CM coding system consists of three volumes:

> Volume 1. Diseases—Tabular List
>
> Volume 2. Diseases—Alphabetic Index
>
> Volume 3. Procedures—Tabular and Alphabetic Index

Physicians need only concern themselves with Volume 1, the tabular list, and Volume 2, the index. Volume 3, which contains codes and descriptions for procedures and an index to these codes, is used almost exclusively by hospitals. Volume 1, the tabular list, contains three-, four-, and five-digit codes and their associated descriptions. Volume 2 is the index to the codes in the tabular list.

The example below, taken from Volume 1, demonstrates a four-digit ICD-9 code:

685.0   Pilonidal cyst w/abscess

In late 1991, the U.S. Government Printing Office released the fourth edition of ICD-9-CM, which incorporates all the changes that were made to ICD-9-CM since the third edition was printed in 1980.

Requirements

A law requiring that all physicians use ICD-9-CM codes when reporting patient diagnoses to Medicare became effective on April 1, 1989. Lack of compliance on claims submitted to Medicare after June 1, 1989, can result in serious penalties ranging from nonpayment of assigned claims to fines of $2,000 per occurrence on unassigned claims.

Although this law applies only to claims submitted to Medicare, the use of ICD-9-CM codes for reporting diagnoses to all third-party payers is advisable for several reasons. First, if diagnosis codes are not used, then payment may be denied or delayed. Second, when the codes are not used, the carrier's staff will locate an ICD-9-CM code based on the physician's description of the patient's problem. This coding is usually performed by individuals with either no or very limited medical background. As a result, the codes selected by the carrier may not logically match the procedure or service being reported, and the claim could be denied.

Finally, many third-party payers have purchased or developed software programs that compare the CPT code to the ICD-9-CM code. These programs test for logical relationships. They would, for example, reveal a mismatch between a procedure listed as the removal of a cyst and the diagnosis as hypertension. Such a claim would probably be automatically denied for lack of medical necessity or reasonableness.

In summary, the three reasons ICD-9-CM diagnosis codes must be reported on claims are as follows:

- Without diagnosis codes, the claim may be delayed or denied.
- The carrier's personnel may assign an incorrect code based on the limited information available to them.
- Computer programs automatically reject mismatched or illogical pairing of diagnosis and procedure codes.

For these reasons, it is becoming increasingly important that physicians become familiar with the ICD-9-CM coding system and its rules. ICD-9-CM code ranges from 001.0 through V82.9 are used to report the reason for treatment. The following sections discuss the organization of the ICD-9-CM coding manual; the use of abbreviations, symbols, and notes; and general coding rules important to physician practices. The discussion is not intended to be exhaustive.

Organization

Volume 1 of ICD-9-CM, the tabular list, contains codes and descriptions for diseases, illnesses, injuries, complaints, symptoms, signs, findings, and so on. It is organized into 17 chapters plus two supplementary sections. The supplementary sections are used for coding patients who are not being seen for a current illness ("V" codes) or when the patient's problem is due to an external cause related to injury or poisoning ("E" codes). Volume 2 of ICD-9-CM is an alphabetic listing of codes used as an index to the first volume.

Codes can be either third digit (category), fourth digit (subcategory), or fifth digit (subclassification). The additional fourth and fifth digits typically provide additional information to the category pertinent to the body area, site, or whether the patient did or did not present complications. An example of each level of code is shown below.

345   Epilepsy

345.0   Generalized nonconvulsive epilepsy

345.01   Generalized nonconvulsive epilepsy w/intractable epilepsy

In this example, **345** is the category. It is further defined by subcategory, in this case that the epilepsy is generalized nonconvulsive. The subcategory is further defined by a fifth-digit subclassification, in this case that the patient has intractable epilepsy with the generalized nonconvulsive epilepsy.

Note: Fifth-digit assignment is not optional—*you must always code to the greatest level of specificity.*

Symbols, Abbreviations, and Notations

The commercial publishers of ICD-9-CM books use a variety of symbols and color coding systems to indicate when additional fourth and or fifth digits are required. The introductory material in these books should be read carefully so that these symbols are understood. In many instances, definitions for the fifth digits are found on the pages preceding the code.

There are two abbreviations in ICD-9-CM, NEC and NOS. Each has a specific meaning and importance to coding and reimbursement. *NEC,* which means "*not elsewhere classified,*" is used when the coder lacks the information necessary to code the term to a more specific category. The ICD-9-CM index provides references to specific codes when such cases arise, and uses the NEC abbreviation to help guide the coder. In other cases, there may not be a code that completely describes the patient's condition. NECs will also be used in these situations.

The *NOS* abbreviation, which means "*not otherwise specified,*" appears throughout the tabular list and is frequently associated with the "unspecified" codes. In fact, "not otherwise specified" means the same as "unspecified." For example, suppose a patient is seen by his/her physician for ringworm, but the type is unknown. In this case, you would code as follows:

110.9   Dermatophytosis site NOS

When codes for unspecified conditions are reported to third-party payers, special attention may need to be given to the claim if reimbursement is expected. Many carriers will often suspend for review claims that list an unspecified diagnosis code. Therefore, you may need to attach a brief note to the claim explaining the patient's problem in more detail.

ICD-9-CM also uses notations to further assist the coder in selecting the appropriate code. *Nonessential modifiers* are one type of notation. In the index, main terms are shown in boldface type. The main term may be followed by a term or group of terms enclosed in parentheses. These terms are called nonessential modifiers because they may or may not appear in the diagnostic statement in order for the code to be used.

For example, under the main term "Encephalitis" in the index, seven nonessential modifiers are listed next to the main term, as shown below:

Encephalitis   (bacterial) (chronic) (hemorrhage) (idiopathic)
(nonepidemic) (spurious) (subacute)

If the diagnostic statement contained one of these terms (for example, the patient has bacterial encephalitis), code **323.9** could be used. Conversely, if the diagnostic statement did not contain one of these terms, it could still be appropriate to use the code, depending on the circumstances. The nonessential modifiers give some examples of specific types of disorders that can be classified under this main term.

Essential modifiers, on the other hand, are indented line entries following the main term. They can represent differences in etiology, site, or other circumstances. For example, the main term "Burn" is followed by the subterm "arm(s)."

Another frequently used notation is the term *see also*. Found in the index and always printed in italics, this notation instructs the coder to refer to another category in addition to the one that the coder is referencing. For example, if you want to code toxic uninodular goiter, you might first look under "Toxic" in the Index. Under "Toxic" you will be instructed to "*see also* condition." So you would look under the entry for the condition (in this case, goiter) to begin locating the proper code.

Notes

ICD-9-CM uses notes to convey information. There are two types of notes—those appearing with groups of codes and those appearing with specific codes. Each type has a specific meaning in ICD-9-CM.

The first type of notes are "Includes" notes. These notes further define or give an example of the contents of a group of codes. Consider the following code from ICD-9-CM:

> **682**   Other Cellulitis and Abscess
>   Includes: Abscess (acute), cellulitis (diffuse),
>   lymphangitis, acute (with lymphangitis) except of
>   finger or toe

These types of abscess or cellulitis could be coded using listings from the **682** series.

The second type of notes, "Excludes" notes, means just the opposite of Includes notes. In ICD-9-CM, the term *Excludes* is always surrounded by a printed box so that it is easily noticed. Coders need to be aware of conditions that are excluded from groups of codes; therefore, they should take notice of the Excludes notes. Here is an example of an Excludes note:

> **737.0**   Adolescent postural kyphosis
>   Excludes: Osteochondrosis of spine (juvenile) **(730.0)**;
>   Adult **(732.8)**

Thus, if a patient is suffering from adult postural kyphosis, codes from the **737** group would not be reported.

In addition to the Includes and Excludes notes, you may also find notes at the beginning of a section of codes and/or at the beginning of a chapter. These notes provide general coding guidance regarding the codes they precede. For example, five paragraphs of notes appear before the **369** group of codes for blindness and low vision. Referring to Chapter 2, Neoplasms, you will find extensive notes related to coding neoplasms. It is important to check for and read notes preceding codes as the notes may affect your code selection.

Tables

There are three tables the coder should be aware of in the index—the Hypertension Table, the Table of Neoplasms, and the Table of Drugs and Chemicals.

1. The *Hypertension Table* is found in the index by looking up the term *hypertension*. It is further broken down by concurrent disease or state, such as pregnancy. Note that there are three columns next to each entry that designate the hypertension state by:

   — Malignant

   — Benign

   — Unspecified

2. The *Neoplasm Table* is found in Volume 2 and has a special listing for neoplasms. It is broken down into four main categories:

   • **Malignant**—a severe form of neoplasm possessing the property for destructive growth and metastasis.

   • **Benign**—a nonmalignant neoplasm.

   • **Uncertain behavior**—pathology has been unable to determine type of neoplasm due to features that are present.

   • **Unspecified**—physician has insufficient data to be able to categorize the neoplasm.

The malignant designation may be further classified by whether the neoplasm is primary, secondary, or cancer in situ.

3. The *Table of Drugs and Chemicals* is found in Volume 2, Section 2. This table contains a classification of drugs and other chemical substances to identify poisoning states and external causes of adverse effects.

Cross-Reference Terms

Cross-reference terms are found in the alphabetic index and instruct the coder to search elsewhere in the ICD-9-CM manual before assigning a code. The three types of terms are *see, see also,* and *see category.* The *see* cross-reference directs the coder to an alternative term. The *see also* term directs the coder to look under another main term in the index, if all the information needed is not found under the first main term. The third type of cross-reference, *see category,* directs the coder to a specific category in the tabular list.

General ICD-9-CM Coding Guidelines

The process of coding with ICD-9-CM is much easier when the coder follows these steps:

1. Review the entire medical record. Do not code from just the face sheet with a list of diagnoses and procedures. Query the physician if the information in the medical record is not consistent.

2. Review all subterms and look first in the alphabetic index for the main term, and then refer to any applicable notes for the term, nonessential modifiers. Follow any cross-reference instructions.

3. Always verify the code numbers in the tabular list. Read and follow instructional terms and notes.

4. Code only three-digit codes for diseases if there are no fourth- or fifth-digit codes available.

5. Code only four-digit codes if there are no fifth-digit codes available.

6. Look for and be guided by the Includes and Excludes notes throughout the code book. These may appear after a particular code or under category section titles.

7. When assigning multiple diagnoses, always sequence the principal diagnosis first.

Fourth- and Fifth-Digit Codes

In many cases, there will be fourth- and fifth-digit codes from which to select. If there is a five-digit code, it must be used. If there is no five-digit code, but there is a four-digit code, use a four-digit code. Use a three-digit code only if there are no four- or five-digit codes.

Fourth-digit codes are expanded completely below the category to which they apply. For example, in the **556** series of codes for ulcerative colitis, four-digit codes are provided, such as:

556.5   Left-sided ulcerative (chronic) colitis

556.6   Universal ulcerative (chronic) colitis

556.8   Other ulcerative colitis

556.9   Ulcerative colitis, unspecified

In some cases, there are as many as ten (0 through 9) fourth-digit codes provided; in others, there may be only one or two. Also, fourth-digit codes do not always follow strict numerical order.

Fifth-digit codes are presented in two different ways in ICD-9-CM. First, each fifth-digit code may be listed as found under the series **054.1** "Genital herpes."

All possible fifth-digit codes are listed. (In this instance, there are five fifth-digit codes to choose from.) The second method involves printing the fifth digits themselves, with their definitions, immediately above the fourth-digit codes to which they apply, like this:

The following fifth-digit subclassification is for use with category **531**:

    0   **without mention of obstruction**

    1   **with obstruction**

These are applied to the fourth-digit codes in the subcategory as appropriate. For example, if the patient has an acute gastric ulcer with perforation and obstruction, the correct code would be **531.11**.

Many carriers' computer systems can identify claims containing ICD-9-CM codes that require fourth or fifth digits. Claims not listing fifth- or fourth-digit diagnosis codes when required may be denied.

Symptoms, Signs, and Ill-Defined Conditions

Some patients may present symptoms or signs that defy immediate diagnosis. Nonetheless, if a claim is filed, a diagnosis must be listed. Special codes can be used in such cases. Chapter 16 in ICD-9-CM provides codes for these types of conditions. For example, a physician is treating a patient who has burning and prickling sensations in his feet. Until a more definitive diagnosis is established, code **782.0**, "Disturbance of skin sensation," can be listed.

It is important to understand that, in the absence of a definitive diagnosis, it is appropriate and preferable to list the symptom or other presenting problem. There can be legal consequences for those who list a code just to obtain payment, or for those who list a diagnosis when the diagnosis is not attested to or documented by the physician. Instead, list the code for the symptom. For example, the patient presents with pain during urination, blood in the urine, slight fever, and back pain. The physician suspects bladder tumors, but is unsure. Until he or she is sure of the diagnosis, the symptoms can be listed as the diagnosis, all of which will support the need for services, such as an office visit.

V Codes

These codes, which begin with the letter V, appear toward the end of Volume 1 under the title "Supplementary Classification of Factors Influencing Health Status and Contact With Health Services." They are typically used when the patient is being seen for something other than a current illness or injury.

A follow-up visit related to a history of major cardiovascular surgery that occurred four years ago would be an example.

E Codes

These codes are supplementary and are used to describe external causes of injuries, poisonings, or other adverse effects. They are never reported by themselves, and they are rarely used by physicians. E codes are located in Volume 2 under Index to External Cause.

In the next chapter we discuss the patient insurance accounting processes involved in submitting a clean insurance claim and managing accounts through to complete payment.

Coding Under Capitation

Coding is necessary under capitation because it drives cost management and cost centers. All CPT codes or a list of all services included or excluded in the capitation rate must be in the contract.

In a managed care setting, codes can be used as a productivity measure for monetary rewards or continuing in the program. In many instances an RVU system is used.

4 Insurance Processing— Managing Insurance and Patient Accounts

Objectives

After completing this chapter, you should be able to:

- Explain the pre–claim submission operations process

- Recognize and describe the use of the different types of forms to include:

  - Patient information

  - Insurance coverage verification

  - Employer information

  - Assignment of benefits

  - Authorization to release medical-related information

  - Signature on file

  - Fact sheet

  - Medical cost estimate

  - Advance notice for elective surgery

  - Waivers of liability

- Recognize and describe the use of the different types of insurance letters to include:

  - Welcome

  - Filing supplemental claims

  - Deductible

Introduction

With the knowledge of the different types of insurance and the ability to code services for reimbursement, the practice must now be able to report to the insurance plan the services provided so it receives appropriate reimbursement.

Unfortunately, this is often easier said than done. Because of the different types of health plans and changing reimbursement methods, the health insurance industry does not follow a set of "universal policies" that standardize or simplify the claim submission process. Each insurance plan usually has its own set of policies and procedures for claim adjudication, and medical practices are expected to understand and adhere to them if they are to receive payment for services rendered.

In this chapter we discuss the "preclaim" insurance processes necessary to manage insurance claim processing from collecting data to claim submission for appropriate payment. We also describe and present sample forms that will help simplify your data collection operations and report formats to increase your information management efficiency.

Pre-Claim Submission Operations

Before any type of claim can be generated and submitted for payment, your office staff needs to perform a number of preclaim tasks critical to assure the validity and accuracy of the patient's billing data and submission of a "clean claim."

The basic objectives of office staff preclaim operations are to:

1. Collect the patient's and responsible parties' information completely and accurately

2. Determine the appropriate financial class or account type (for example, commercial insurance, Medicare, Medicaid), and correctly assign primary and secondary insurance billing status when two insurance plans require coordination of benefits

3. Educate the patient as to his or her ultimate financial responsibility for services rendered, and obtain written waivers when necessary to support future collection efforts

4. Verify all data collected before rendering services or submitting claims, and obtain updated profiles of insurance plan benefits using an "insurance/employer verification form"

5. Anticipate the need for collection through accounts receivable controls and quality data

The basic pre-claim submission operations include:

- Appointments/preregistration
- Registration/patient demographic and insurance verification
- Patient education of payment policies and credit screening/financial arrangements

- Entry of patient data
- Capture of all billable services and transaction entry
- Claims processing and submission

The following sections in this chapter discuss each of these operations in detail.

Appointments/Preregistration

In most cases, new patients wishing to see a physician will call the physician group to make an appointment. This initial contact by the prospective patient is a perfect time to identify the reason for the visit, begin collecting patient demographic and insurance billing data, and schedule a convenient time for the physician and patient. It is also important to verify patient referral information and make arrangements to get necessary forms and authorizations completed, as applicable.

The need to identify the reason for the visit is important, as most practices have divided their appointment schedule to accommodate lengthy new patient history and physicals during a certain period, procedures during another time slot, and basic follow-up visits throughout the day. If the practice is at capacity, it may take three or more days to obtain an appointment, time that can be spent verifying the patient information.

The patient's demographic and insurance information should be obtained during the initial telephone contact through a polite telephone interview and recorded using a patient information form.

A good practice is to call the patient one or two days before the scheduled appointment, as a reminder. In some instances this will assist the patient who has forgotten or allow the practice to fill slots that may have gone unused. This is also a good time to gather information or remind patients of the necessary information they will need to bring for their visit.

Patient Information Form

The patient information form is a vital document used to gather necessary demographic data about a patient, such as name, address, guardian or responsible party name, insurance company and health plan policy information, the name of the person or physician who referred the patient to the practice, and so on.

This form does not include any information related to medical conditions; it is usually only for insurance and payment-related information and/or for general marketing data. This form should be completed when a *patient first visits the practice, and at least once every year,* because approximately 20 percent of people move each year. In this way, the practice may keep its records current.

Typically, practices design the information form to fit on an 8½ x 11 inch (standard size) paper with plenty of space allowed for patients to complete required information accurately (see Exhibit 4.1).

Not only is the patient information form valuable for gathering important insurance processing information, but it is also a way of tracking and finding patients who become delinquent in their payments. Additional information, such as secondary insurance coverage, and special circumstances, such as divorce, can also be gathered.

Give the patient information about the practice and collect as much patient information as possible on insurance coverage, including any toll-free numbers for eligibility verification and filing requirements. During the initial contact with the prospective patient, the office staff may want to communicate policies to and obtain information from the patient:

- Basic services for the condition and physicians' fees
- The patient's financial responsibility for services provided during the initial visit
- An estimate of the costs associated with a new-comprehensive history and physical examination
- How the patient will be paying for the initial visit (HMO/PPO co-pay, cash, check, credit card)
- Future visit payment policy
- Whether the patient needs financial counseling before the visit

After the reason for the visit from the potential patient is identified, a tentative patient care plan is developed so all procedures and services planned for in the care plan (office visit, laboratory, surgery, injection, etc.) can be verified for service coverage. All information obtained will be reviewed by the account manager/office manager to determine the prospective account's financial class, potential collectibility, credit-worthiness, and the need for patient-related financial counseling.

Registration/Demographic and Insurance Coverage Verification

The importance of patient registration in capturing accurate information, including referring physician data and verifying all information provided by the patient, is an area often overlooked by staff responsible for billing because of time or perceived value. Demographic, financial, and referring physician information should be obtained.

Exhibit 4.1   New Patient's Information Sheet

PATIENT INFORMATION

Name: (First) _____ (MI) _____ (Last) _____

Date of Birth _____ Age _____ Sex: ☐ M ☐ F   Marital Status: ☐ S ☐ M ☐ W ☐ D

Address: (Street) _____

(City, State, ZIP) _____

Phone #: _____ Social Security #: _____ Driver License #: _____

Work #: _____ Employer: _____

Employer's Address: _____

Referring Physician: _____ If Student, School Name: _____ Full/Part Time _____

RESPONSIBLE PARTY OR SPOUSE INFORMATION

Name: _____ Relationship to Patient: _____

Address: (Street) _____

(City, State, ZIP) _____

Phone #: _____ Social Security #: _____ Driver License #: _____

Work #: _____ Employer: _____

Employer's Address: _____

Friend or Relative Not Living with You: _____ Phone #: _____

INSURANCE INFORMATION

Medicare #: _____ Medicaid #: _____

Insurance Co: _____ Phone #: _____

Insurance Address: _____

Group #: _____ Certificate or I.D. #: _____

Insured's Name: _____ Relationship to Patient: ☐ Self ☐ Spouse ☐ Dependent

Insured's Employer: _____ Phone #: _____

Employer's Address: _____

Insured's Social Security #: _____ Date of Birth: _____ Sex: ☐ M ☐ F

If the patient it covered by another insurance policy, please complete the following information for coordination of benefits. This information will enable your insurance company to process your claim more quickly. Thank you!

INSURANCE INFORMATION

Insurance Co: _____ Phone #: _____

Insurance Address: _____

Group #: _____ Certificate or I.D. #: _____

Insured's Name: _____ Relationship to Patient: ☐ Self ☐ Spouse ☐ Dependent

Insured's Employer: _____ Phone #: _____

Employer's Address: _____

Insured's Social Security #: _____ Date of Birth: _____ Sex: ☐ M ☐ F

I hereby assign, transfer, and set over to {Name of Practice} all of my rights, title, and interest to my medical reimbursement benefits under my insurance policy. I authorize the release of any medical information needed to determine these benefits. This authorization shall remain valid until written notice is given by me revoking said authorization. I understand that I am financially responsible for all charges whether or not they are covered by insurance.

Patient's Signature _____ Date _____

Today, change is constant, so the need to obtain information for verification becomes more necessary. Insurance coverage or eligibility for public medical programs changes from one month to the next for thousands of Americans. The use of forged health insurance ID cards for health care is a new problem with which practices must now deal.

Practices must keep in mind that they are, in a broad sense, providers of "good-faith credit" for medical service rendered to patients. Too often, patients are extended "credit" without adequate review of their credit-worthiness or a discussion of their ultimate financial responsibility.

The patient's registration information serves not only as the foundation for billing and collection, but also as a tool for credit-granting decisions made by the practice. The collectibility of each patient account, whether by insurance or self-pay, is only as strong as the information obtained from the patient, its verification for accuracy, and the patient's understanding of his or her financial obligations.

In most practices, the registration information provided by the patient on the demographic form is rarely verified for accuracy and completeness. The verification of all patient demographic and insurance information is a process that must be instituted to:

- Confirm patient insurance coverage for the service to be rendered and to determine primary and secondary coordination of benefit coverage, which allows for accurate billing of covered services

- Serve as a quality assurance tool for correctly processing billing information (ultimately responsible for the success of collections)

- Serve as an indicator in identifying patients who need financial counseling or assistance with obtaining medical assistance for services rendered

- Reduce unnecessary write-offs and negative adjustments for uncollectible charges due to denials, down-coding, or reduced payment because of nonverified coverage of services

To reach the objectives listed above, *all practices must implement a process of information/verification.* We suggest that all patients undergo a thorough verification of all demographic, financial, and insurance coverage information they submit.

The verification coordinator must identify the primary carrier for proper coordination of benefits. Contact the primary insurance plan first to confirm coverage of the patient's services using the insurance coverage verification forms.

When verifying insurance coverage, remember that each category of physician (medicine, surgery, primary care) will ask about coverage and payment policies for services he or she performs relative to the patient's condition.

The office should verify all insurance information in each of the following situations:

- If the patient is to be admitted to the hospital or subjected to an outpatient surgical procedure
- If the patient will have many visits to the office over an extended period of time
- If the patient will undergo a minor diagnostic or therapeutic procedure in the office
- If the office believes the patient may have deductible responsibilities
- If the office believes the patient's insurance may have changed or terminated
- For established patients, at least once a year, preferably between October and January

Employer Information/Insurance Verification Form

To be used in addition to the patient information form, this form provides specific information about the type and extent of insurance coverage the patient receives from his/her employer. This form is more discretionary. Some practices may find the additional information helpful while others may find that the information gathered on the patient information form is adequate. Two different formats are shown in Exhibits 4.2 and 4.3.

How to Verify Insurance Coverage

The business support staff of a medical practice should be responsible for the verification of all patient demographics and insurance plan coverage for all services likely to be provided in the patient's care plan, before the initiation of such services. The process is explained below:

1. Before a patient is admitted to the practice, and before the initiation of services, the social support staff will obtain:

   - Demographic and insurance information from the prospective patient using the patient demographic form. The patient demographic form should be filled out by (1) interviewing the patient over the phone, (2) having the patient fill out the form through the mail, or (3) having the patient complete it at admission

Exhibit 4.2   Employer/Insurance Verification Information Form

Date: _____

Employer Name: _____

Employer Address: _____

Benefits Coordinator: _____ Phone: _____

Insurance Carrier: _____ Plan Name: _____

Policy #: _____ Plan #: _____ Group #: _____

Type of Plan: ☐ Traditional ☐ 80/20 ☐ HMO ☐ PPO ☐ Other: _____

Mail Insurance Forms to: ☐ Carrier   ☐ Employer

Billing Address: _____

Contact Person: _____ Phone Number: _____

Renewal Period – Medical Benefits and Limits Are Renewed on (M/D/Y): (Date): _____

Basic Coverage

Physician Payment Schedule: ☐ UCR ☐ RBRVS ☐ Other Data

Percentage of COB (ie, 80/20?): _____ % Insurance Coverage _____ % Patient Copayment

Annual Outpatient Deductible: _____ Amount of Deductible Remaining: _____

Maximum Benefit: _____

Noncovered Services: _____

Diagnostic Benefits

Percentage of COB (ie, 80/20?): _____ % Insurance Coverage _____ % Patient Copayment

Annual Outpatient Deductible: _____ Amount of Deductible Remaining: _____

Maximum Benefit: _____

Noncovered Services: _____

Major Medical Coverage

Annual Outpatient Deductible: _____

Amount of Deductible Remaining: _____

Maximum Benefit: _____

Noncovered Services: _____

Form Used: ☐ Company-Specific Form ☐ HCFA-1500

Notes: _____

_____

_____

Exhibit 4.3   **Patient Insurance Coverage Verification Form**

Date: _____ Practice: _____ Verification By: _____

Patient Name: _____ Account #: _____

Date of Birth: _____ Social Security #: _____

Employer: _____ Phone/Contact: _____

Accident Date: _____ Accident Location: _____

Patient Care Plan

Dx: (1) _____ (2) _____

Dx: (3) _____ (4) _____

Patient Care Plans/Services: _____

Insurance Data

Insurance – 1

Billing Address: _____

Ins. Contact Name: _____ Phone: _____

Policy #: _____ Plan: _____ Group: _____

Coverage Effective Dates – (From) _____ (To) _____

Policyholder: _____ Relationship: _____

Insurance – 2

Billing Address: _____

Ins. Contact Name: _____ Phone: _____

Policy #: _____ Plan: _____ Group: _____

Coverage Effective Dates – (From) _____ (To) _____

Policyholder: _____ Relationship: _____

Basic Benefits	**Primary**	**Secondary**
1. Preexisting Wait Period		
2. Annual Deductible Amount	($)	
3. Deductible Paid to Date		
4. Out-of-Pocket Expenses:		
a. Coinsurance ($ or %)		
b. Copayment @ TOS?		
5. Calendar Year Maximum:	$ ____ / ____ days	$ ____ / ____ days
6. Lifetime Maximum:	$ ____ / ____ days	$ ____ / ____ days
7. Remaining Benefits:	$ ____ / ____ days	$ ____ / ____ days
8. Medical Records Required?	Y / N	Y / N
9. Coordinate Benefits (X-Over)?	Y / N	Y / N
10. 2nd Opinion Requirements?	Y / N	Y / N
11. Verified with (name):		
12. Phone # of Above:		
13. Date Verified:		

Procedures & Services	**Covered?**	**Coverage Details / Limits**
1. Office Services	Y / N	
2. Hospital	Y / N	
3. Consultations	Y / N	
4. ER Visits	Y / N	
5. Laboratory (Chem)	Y / N	
6. Procedures	Y / N	
7. Injections / Tx	Y / N	
8. Supplies	Y / N	
9. Drugs / Medications	Y / N	
10. Exclusions:		

- Copies of hospital admission and patient information (if applicable)
- Copies of all insurance cards (front and back)
- Copy of guarantor's driver's license (front only)
- Information on insurance plan coverage and the order of benefit coordination (that is, primary, secondary, or tertiary)

2. From the above information, the practice staff will verify all patient demographic and insurance policy coverage information through telephone contacts and cross-referencing information from different sources.

- Patient and guarantor addresses are to be cross-referenced with telephone directories, postal addresses, driver's licenses, employment confirmation, and other sources of current information.
- Each insurance plan identified by the patient is to be contacted by telephone to verify insurance coverage for patient services using one of the insurance coverage verification forms (ICVFs).
- Insurance plan coverage is to be verified one plan at a time, making sure to complete the insurance data section, benefits grid section, and the service coverage listing for all services pertinent to your practice that need to be verified for coverage.

3. Only confirmed and verified information is to be entered on the ICVF. Changes to the patient source document are to be made in red pen, initialed, and dated.

4. Insurance plan coverage(s) that cannot be verified must have the reason indicated on the ICVF report.

5. After all policy coverage(s) have been verified, the completed ICVF should be copied. The original is placed in the patient's chart. The copy should be stored in a three-ring binder labeled "Insurance/Employer Health Plan Profiles." Store the information alphabetically by insurance or employer name, and update the profiles for future reference.

Overview of the Patient Insurance Coverage Verification Form (ICVF)

Basic Patient Demographic Data Section   The top section of the form is used to track the start and completion of the entire ICVF report for each new patient.

Date—Enter the date the verification process was initiated and completed.

Practice—Enter the practice name (helpful for multispecialty practices).

Verification By—Enter the name of the verification clerk.

Patient Name/Account Number—Enter patient's name and add practice account number later.

Date of Birth—Enter the patient's date of birth.

Social Security Number—Enter the patient's Social Security number.

Employer—Enter the name of the patient's employer.

Phone/Contact—Enter the contact name and phone number for benefits management.

Accident Date—If services are related to an accident (auto, workers' compensation, etc.), enter the date of the accident.

Accident Location—Define where the injury occurred/location.

Patient Care Plan Section   This section maintains the clinical data needed to begin inquiry as to coverage and benefits. The patient's reason for the appointment or previously confirmed diagnoses from another physician for which the patient will be seen (as in the case of a consultation) should be entered here, as well as possible services—both diagnostic and therapeutic—that may/will be performed.

Dx: (1)—Enter the patient's primary diagnosis or complaint.

Dx: (2)—Enter the patient's secondary diagnosis or complaint.

Dx: (3)—Enter the patient's third diagnosis or complaint.

Dx: (4)—Enter the patient's fourth diagnosis or complaint.

Patient Care Plans/Services—List the possible services that may be performed on this patient.

Insurance Data Section   This section is used to record and then verify insurance plan information provided by the patient for future billing and coordination of the patient's benefits. All insurance plans submitted by the patient are to be verified individually. **Note:** It is extremely important to assign the proper order of multiple insurance plan coverages (that is, primary plan versus secondary plan).

Insurance–(1)—Enter the name of the carrier that has identified itself as the primary insurance plan.

Phone—Enter the carrier's phone number(s).

Billing Address—Enter the carrier's billing address.

Ins. Contact Name—Enter the name of the insurance representative.

Phone—Enter the insurance contact's direct line and extension.

Policy Number—Enter the patient's verified policy number.

Plan—Enter the patient's verified plan number.

Group—Enter the patient's verified group number.

Coverage Effective Dates—Enter insurance plan effective dates of coverage, identifying (From) date and (To) date.

Policyholder—Enter verified policyholder's name.

Relationship—Verify relationship of patient to policyholder.

Note: After each insurance plan is verified one at a time, carefully complete the next section, the Benefits Section.

Basic Benefits Section   This section is developed like a grid to capture all insurance plan(s) information and for easy review of all plan benefits. The grid is divided into three columns, one for the insurance benefit question and one for each insurance plan—primary and secondary.

1. Preexisting Wait Period:
    Some policies do not provide benefits for certain conditions for a predetermined period of time. Example: A 12-month waiting period for maternity (that is, no benefits until plan is more than 12 months into effect). Enter Y or N. Note: Some health plan policies do not provide benefits for certain conditions, diagnoses, or preexisting conditions. If this is the case, indicate "noncovered" on the space provided.

2. Annual Deductible Amount:
    What is the insurance plan's annual deductible amount (amount patient must pay out-of-pocket before insurance will start to cover services)? Enter the annual deductible dollar amount.

3. Deductible Paid to Date:
    How much has the patient paid toward the deductible to date (as of today)? Enter the deductible amount paid to date. **Note:** The difference is collectible at time of service.

4. Out-of-Pocket Expenses:
    Does the plan have a patient cost-sharing program that may include co-payment or co-insurance provisions?

    a. Co-insurance = Dollar amount or percentage of patient financial responsibility, or

    b. Co-payment @ TOS = The collection of a co-payment at time of service, usually $5 to $15 per visit (see insurance card).

5. Calendar Year Maximum:
   Enter the dollar amount and/or the number of days limited by the insurance policy as a total annual payable benefit, if applicable.

6. Lifetime Maximum:
   Enter the maximum dollar amount and/or the number of days allowed by the insurance policy as a total payable benefit, if applicable.

7. Remaining Benefits:
   Enter the dollar amount and/or the number of days available under the insurance policy for remaining payable benefits, if applicable.

8. Medical Records Required:
   Are medical records or other supporting documents required for claim processing and receiving payment for services rendered? Enter Y or N. If yes, make note on expanded insurance information sheet (page 2, 3, or 4).

9. Coordinate Benefits (X-Over):
   Will the primary policy coordinate or cross over the benefits with any secondary insurance? Enter Y or N.

10. Second Opinion Requirements:
    Does the plan have second opinion requirements for specific conditions before payment of service benefits? Enter Y or N.

11. Verified with (name):
    Enter the name of the person from the insurance plan to whom the verification clerk has been speaking to identify policy coverage.

12. Phone Number of Above:
    Enter the phone number of the person from the insurance plan to whom the verification clerk has been speaking to identify policy coverage.

13. Date Verified:
    Enter date the above information was verified.

Procedures and Services Section   This section is designed to capture individual insurance policy coverage information for all services that may be provided by your physicians and practice. Obviously, the services to be verified for coverage will vary by specialty, so think about the services your practice would need to verify most frequently.

Each insurance plan representative contacted should be asked to provide coverage information on anticipated service that potential patients will likely receive. When interviewing each insurance representative:

- Ask the questions listed below for each service
- Indicate on the report if the policy provides coverage (Y or N)
- Indicate if the policy has limitations or maximum coverage amounts
- Ask what code it requires for payment of the service—compare this CPT code to the one listed to the right of the description
- Ask about any service limitations, coverage, or service exclusions
- Ask what is the maximum reimbursement amount for each procedure

Special coding or payment policies that may affect reimbursement should be inquired about as well, particularly for surgery-related practices. Some additional questions to ask include the following:

- Do they use the current CPT Book (199_)?
- When must the new CPT codes be used (that is, effective date)?
- How is payment allowance based? (Please send copy of allowance data.)
- How does their plan define "global surgical package" and "global surgical periods"?
- Are complications from surgery bundled in postoperative care or can treatment be reported separately with appropriate modifiers?
- Are there any reductions in payment if a procedure is performed in an outpatient hospital setting?
- How are multiple surgical procedures reimbursed? First__, second__, third__, fourth__, fifth or more___
- What are their supply payment policies? Are HCPCS codes required or is 99070 acceptable?
- How are injectable drugs reimbursed and how should they be reported (J-codes)?

Remember to document as much pertinent information about the policy coverage as possible, as the verification document serves as the ultimate quality assurance tool for billing and collections.

Only after a thorough verification of the patient's insurance plan coverage, the assignment of an unquestioned financial classification or account type, and having obtained signed agreements with the patient concerning financial obligation should a patient be admitted to your practice. All questionable information should be reviewed by the account manager to determine the prospective account's financial class, potential collectibility, credit-worthiness, and the need for patient-related financial counseling and/or service deposit calculations.

The patient's demographic information on the patient and guarantor can be cross-referenced and verified through multiple reference sources, including:

1. Telephone directory or directory assistance

2. Social Security office

3. Post office

4. Annual city directory (R. L. Polk)—approx. $120

5. Personal bank

6. Employer

7. Driver's license—contact Department of Motor Vehicles; requires name, date of birth, Social Security number, and driver's license number

8. County court offices—Legal or Auditor Department (all public records)

Registration–Date of Service

Most physician offices have a sign-in sheet at the reception window. While some practices use pharmaceutical notepads to sign patients in, a formal sign-in sheet will provide the practice with a constant source of valuable information that will enhance practice operations. A sample sign-in sheet is shown in Exhibit 4.4.

The sample format of the sign-in sheet provides information about whether the patient is new or established; changes in address, employer, and insurance; and waiting time efficiency data based on appointment time and arrival data.

After the patient signs in, the coordinator should greet the patient and review the sign-in sheet. If the patient is a new patient, he or she should be given the patient demographic information form on a clipboard and asked to complete it. Some practices also give the patient a medical history form to complete, which is incorporated into the patient's medical record.

The registration coordinator should ask to make photocopies of the patient's:

- Insurance card—front and back
- Special billing forms
- Driver's license

Exhibit 4.4   Sample Sign-In Sheet

Welcome — Please Sign In

Date _____

Patient name (add current address if changed)	Arrival time	Time of appoint-ment	Physician to be seen	Are you a new patient? (circle one)	Has information changed since last visit?			Office use only	
					Address (circle one)	Employer (circle one)	Insurance (circle one)	Call time	Superbill number
1				Y / N	Y / N	Y / N	Y / N		
2				Y / N	Y / N	Y / N	Y / N		
3				Y / N	Y / N	Y / N	Y / N		
4				Y / N	Y / N	Y / N	Y / N		
5				Y / N	Y / N	Y / N	Y / N		
6				Y / N	Y / N	Y / N	Y / N		
7				Y / N	Y / N	Y / N	Y / N		
8				Y / N	Y / N	Y / N	Y / N		
9				Y / N	Y / N	Y / N	Y / N		
10				Y / N	Y / N	Y / N	Y / N		
11				Y / N	Y / N	Y / N	Y / N		
12				Y / N	Y / N	Y / N	Y / N		
13				Y / N	Y / N	Y / N	Y / N		
14				Y / N	Y / N	Y / N	Y / N		
15				Y / N	Y / N	Y / N	Y / N		
16				Y / N	Y / N	Y / N	Y / N		
17				Y / N	Y / N	Y / N	Y / N		
18				Y / N	Y / N	Y / N	Y / N		
19				Y / N	Y / N	Y / N	Y / N		
20				Y / N	Y / N	Y / N	Y / N		
21				Y / N	Y / N	Y / N	Y / N		
22				Y / N	Y / N	Y / N	Y / N		
23				Y / N	Y / N	Y / N	Y / N		
24				Y / N	Y / N	Y / N	Y / N		
25				Y / N	Y / N	Y / N	Y / N		

The patient information form shown in Exhibit 4.1 has a series of statements at the bottom. The patient must read, sign, and date it. The statement states:

"I hereby assign, transfer, and set over to [name of practice] *all of my rights, title, and interest to my medical reimbursement benefits under my insurance policy. I authorize the release of any medical information needed to determine these benefits. This authorization shall remain valid until written notice is given by me revoking said authorization. I understand that I am financially responsible for all charges whether or not they are covered by insurance."*

This statement informs the patient that:

1. He or she has "assigned" or transferred the right of direct reimbursement from any health plan, including those that involve nonparticipating physicians, to the practice so the reimbursement can be mailed directly to the practice.

2. He or she has given authorization to release any medical record information needed to coordinate benefits and reimbursement.

3. The authorization is enforced unless he or she is otherwise notified.

4. He or she understands his or her financial responsibility for charges for services rendered.

While the patient information form serves the practice's internal needs, the practice should *obtain patient or guarantor signatures* on the following forms for the following insurance types:

From Patients With Commercial Insurance:

- Authorization to release medical-related information
- Assignment of benefits and payment to provider

From Patients With Medicare:

- Authorization to pay Medicare benefits (signature on file)
- Authorization to release medical-related information
- Assignment of benefits and payment to provider

From Patients With Blue Cross and Blue Shield/Managed Care Plans:

- Authorization to release medical-related information
- Assignment of benefits and payment to provider

Assignment of Benefits and Payment to Provider Form

The assignment of benefits and payment to provider form is used as authorization by patients to their insurance plan to send the check directly to the provider. This form is required when the providers are rendering services to patients with insurance plans that the provider(s) are *not participating* in. A sample is shown in Exhibit 4.5.

When a provider is not participating in an insurer's plan, the checks are usually mailed to the patient or policyholder, making collection more difficult. It is also used if the patient's policy prohibits direct payment to the provider. Send this letter as a legal document to receive direct payment.

The insurer will likely take one of three actions after receiving the authorization:

1. Send payment to the practice in the name of the practice.

2. Send payment to the practice in the name of the patient.

3. Refuse to send check to practice and continue sending the check(s) to the patient.

When to use: The form should be filled out by the patient on his or her first visit to the practice, if the patient's insurance plan is one in which the provider(s) do not participate, or in cases where the checks are mailed to the patient.

What to do: Complete the form and then have the patient and a witness sign the form. Make a copy and send it with the claim; retain the original in the patient's chart.

Authorization for Release of Medical-Related Information Form

Patient medical information is confidential and private information. It cannot be released without the patient's consent. Because insurance companies sometimes need to refer to medical information before making a determination on a claim, you will need to have patients sign an authorization to release medical information such as the authorization for release of medical-related information form. See Exhibit 4.6.

Signature on File Form

Rather than having the patient sign each claim form being submitted, most practices have the patient sign a "blanket" statement, called a signature on file form. By obtaining the patient's signature on this form, the practice can enter

Exhibit 4.5   **Assignment and Instruction for
Direct Payment to Medical Providers**

Private – Group Accident – Health Insurance Authorization of Benefits

Patient: _____

Policyholder: _____

Employer: _____   Group #: _____

Social Security #: _____   Policy #: _____

I hereby authorize and instruct that _____ Insurance Company pay
authorized insurance benefits, on my behalf, by check made out and mailed to:

– or –

If my current policy prohibits direct payment to medical provider, then I hereby also instruct and direct you
to make out the check to me and mail it as follows:

     c/o _____

for professional or medical expense benefits allowable, and otherwise payable to me under my current
insurance policy as payment toward the total charges for services rendered. *This is a direct assignment
of my rights and benefits under this policy.* This payment will not exceed my indebtedness to the above
mentioned assignee, and I have agreed to pay, in a current manner, any balance of said professional
service charges over and above this insurance payment amount. A photocopy of this Assignment shall be
considered as effective and valid as the original.

I also authorize the release of information pertinent to my case to any insurance company, adjuster, or
attorney involved in this case.

Signed and dated at the above named practice this _____ day of _____, 199____.

_____
Signature of Policyholder

_____
Witness

_____
Signature of Claimant, if other than Policyholder

the words "signature on file" in the appropriate block of the claim form (on the HCFA-1500, items 12 and 13). This form can also be used to obtain blanket authorization for assignment of benefits. A sample form, acceptable for Medicare and other patients, is shown in Exhibit 4.7.

Exhibit 4.6   **Authorization for Release of Medical-Related Information**

1.   I authorize Dr. _____ to disclose complete information to [name of insurance company] concerning his medical findings and treatment of the undersigned.

2.   Further, I authorize him to testify without limitation, as to all medical findings and the treatment administered to the undersigned, in any legal action, suit, or proceedings to which I am, or may become, a party; and I waive on behalf of myself and any persons who may have an interest in the matter all provisions of law relating to the disclosure of confidential medical information.

   Signed,

_____   _____
Patient   Witness

_____   _____
Date   Place

Exhibit 4.7   **Signature on File Form**

I authorize any holder of medical or other information about me to release to [the Social Security Administration and Health Care Financing Administration or its intermediaries, carriers, and agents or name of insurance company], any information needed to determine the benefits for this or a related claim.

Also, I permit a copy of this authorization to be used in place of the original, and request payment of medical insurance benefits either to myself or to the party who accepts assignment. Regulations pertaining to Medicare assignment of benefits apply.

_____   _____
Signature   Date

Patient Education of Payment Policies

Each practice should have preestablished patient insurance policies and procedures for their office staff and should be able to consistently communicate, explain, and enforce the practice's payment policies to patients.

The goals of informing patients about the practice's insurance policies are to make patients clearly aware of the following:

- In most cases, regardless of insurance status, *patients are ultimately accountable for all or some of their medical bills*, and the amount due must be paid on demand as indicated by the practice.

- Unless the physician is under contract or has signed a participation agreement with a health insurance plan, the contract for the patient's health policy is *between the patient and the health insurer*. While the patient is ultimately financially responsible, the practice will submit the primary insurance on behalf of the patient.

- Insurance does *not usually cover or pay for all medical charges*, and the patient will almost always have some financial obligation for payment.

- Payment problems or *the need for financial counseling* to meet patient financial responsibilities must be brought to the attention of the staff before the rendering of service(s).

In addition, the staff should review some of the basic practice policies covering such issues as the following:

- Does the practice automatically produce a claim form (standard HCFA-1500) for all patients who have a primary insurance plan, or does the automatic claim generation only apply to Medicare or to Medicaid or to Managed Care Plans, and so on?

- How is the coordination of benefits handled? Will the practice process primary payment and then automatically produce a claim form for patients who may have a supplemental insurance plan?

- At what point does the insurance balance overdue become the patient's responsibility? For example, when the office staff is having a difficult time with the collection of payment from third-party payers, the staff should contact the patient to inform him or her of the problem and enlist his or her assistance. Some practices give the patient's insurance 60 days, then the balance is transferred to the patient's responsibility for immediate payment.

Patient Communications

Many practices find it helpful to provide explanatory letters or pamphlets to their patients regarding insurance processing policies. Various sample letters are provided here as guides for your practice.

Welcome/Explanation Letter

Your practice may give a welcome letter to new patients that outlines your practice's insurance processing policies. The policies outlined in the sample letter shown in Exhibit 4.8 may not be appropriate for your practice, but this practice did a good job of explaining their policies to patients. You may want to copy this letter using your practice's policies and guidelines.

Insurance Fact Sheet

An insurance fact sheet is another method of explaining insurance processing requirements to your patients. Considering the many different health insurance policies written today, it would be virtually impossible to create one insurance fact sheet that would serve all your patients. However, you can outline your patients' payment responsibilities and provide them with useful names and phone numbers. A sample of one practice's fact sheet is shown in Exhibit 4.9.

Medical Cost Estimate Form

Knowing what to plan for can lessen the burden of treatment of an illness or injury. Patients about to undergo medical treatment want to have some idea of what the costs will be so they can plan an appropriate budget. Also, by providing them with the required financial information, you increase the odds that the practice will receive prompt reimbursement.

The form shown in Exhibit 4.10 can help you provide them with this valuable information. You may want to contact the offices of other physicians involved in your patient's care, if necessary, to obtain an estimate of their charges.

Required Medicare Forms

In addition to the signature on file form, Medicare requires nonparticipating physicians to have the patient sign two additional forms. The first pertains to elective surgery.

When the nonparticipating physician plans to perform an elective surgery (one that can be scheduled in advance and for which a delay in performing the

Exhibit 4.8   Sample Welcome Letter

Family Medical Group   Lynn I. Hunt, MD

Seattle, Washington   Robert H. Squires, MD

Dear Patient:

If you have health insurance other than those specifically mentioned below, we ask that you pay us and then collect reimbursement from your insurance company. At the time of your clinic visit, you will be provided with a form that contains all the information necessary for you to file your claim with your insurance company. You will also receive a statement of current charges and any balance due each month. An additional copy of this is provided, which you may also use to bill your insurance company for current charges. If there is a problem or if you have a question, please feel free to discuss it with us. We are here to help you with this process.

BC/BS: If you have King County Blue Shield, we will bill King County Blue Shield for the entire amount of your charges. Any charges or balances not covered by King County Blue Shield will be billed directly to you.

Medicaid recipients must present a current, valid card prior to treatment. Any appropriate co-payments or deductibles as determined by your Medicaid eligibility are due at the time of service. Please ask to speak to the bookkeeper regarding questions and payment arrangements.

Medicare patients are asked to pay for services at the time of their visit, unless prior payment arrangements have been made. We will submit your claim to Medicare, and you will receive payment directly from Medicare. If you require help with your billings or have difficulty paying the difference between what is charged and what Medicare pays, please ask to speak with the bookkeeper. Arrangements can be made for those with special needs.

Thank you for coming to our practice. Please tell us if you have any difficulty with your insurance claims.

Sincerely,

Lynn Hunt, MD

Robert Squires, MD

Exhibit 4.9   Insurance Fact Sheet

At the time of your visit, you will be provided with a copy of our encounter form. The pink copy is to be attached to your insurance claim form and mailed to your insurance carrier.

You should follow these steps when completing your insurance claim form:

1. Be sure to fill out the top portion of the claim form.

2. It is not necessary for you to fill in the portions regarding diagnosis or procedures. That information is on the encounter form.

3. Dr. Smith's name, address, and provider number are also on the encounter form. You do not need to add this to the claim form.

4. If you have not already paid for your services, we will anticipate your forwarding the insurance check directly to our office so that we may credit your account. It is not necessary for you to deposit the check. You may simply endorse the back of the check as follows:

   Pay to the order of James Smith, MD

   and send it to our office in the enclosed envelope.

5. If you have a supplemental policy, fill out the top portion of the claim form, attach the Explanation of Medical Benefits (detach from your check), a copy of the encounter form, and mail them. Do not bill your supplemental policy before receiving an Explanation of Medical Benefits from your primary policy.

Helpful phone numbers:

Blue Cross/Blue Shield:_____

Travelers: _____

Medicaid: _____

Metropolitan: _____

Exhibit 4.10   Medical Cost Estimate Form

Patient Name: _____   Date: _____

Explanation of Procedure: _____

_____

	Fee	*% Covered by Insurance*
Surgery:	_____	_____
Assistant Surgeon:	_____	_____
Consultation:	_____	_____
Hospital Visits:	_____	_____
Other Professional Services:	_____	_____
*Anesthesiologist:	_____	_____
*Pathologist:	_____	_____
Total	_____	_____
Approximate Out-of-Pocket Cost	_____	_____

While you are in the hospital, there may be charges for laboratory tests, medications, transfusions, or special care that we are unable to estimate. Be assured that we are sensitive to the rising cost of medical services and will make every effort to deliver quality medical care in the most cost-efficient manner possible, without compromising your good health.

You may wish to contact the hospital business office at _____ for further information about hospital charges. Remember your health insurance card on the day of admittance!

[*You may want to explain that these are required by the hospital for certain surgeries, when applicable.]

procedure does not cause serious damage to the patient), the physician does not accept assignment, and the fee is $500 or greater, the physician must notify the patient, in writing, of the anticipated cost and out-of-pocket expense. A notice for this purpose that is acceptable to Medicare is shown in Exhibit 4.11.

The second form pertains to services deemed by Medicare to be medically unnecessary or that are otherwise noncovered.

When the physician knows that a procedure or service may not be paid for by Medicare because it has been determined to be medically unnecessary to treat a specified condition, or when the physician has a legitimate reason to believe that Medicare will not cover the service, *the physician must notify the patient, in writing*, before providing the service. Therefore, the patient will be required to pay for the service.

The patient must sign this form for it to be considered valid by Medicare, and a new form must be completed for each situation. It is not to be used as a blanket statement. Both participating and nonparticipating physicians are required to provide this form in applicable circumstances (Exhibit 4.12).

Insurance Advanced Notice Service Waiver of Liability

Like the Medicare advanced notice, a similar form can be utilized to notify patients with other insurance plans. This reinforces the patient's understanding of his/her financial responsibility for services to be rendered. Have the patient complete the form and store it in the patient's file (Exhibit 4.13).

Entry of Patient and Insurance Data

For practices that have a computer billing management system, the patient demographic and insurance information is usually entered into the system before the initial date of service encounter and the information has been verified before the encounter. While there are different software billing management programs, most have common data fields that are crucial for error-free insurance billing.

Because of the volume of data needed to process claims, most systems separate the entry of the patient information section from the responsible party section and from the insurance assignment section through separate screens. The patient data for each of these three sections needs to be carefully reviewed and entered into the management system.

Exhibit 4.11   Advance Notice Form for Elective Surgery Over $500

I do not plan to accept assignment for your surgery. The law requires that where assignment is not taken and the charge is $500 or more, the following information must be provided prior to surgery. These estimates assume that you have already met the $100 annual Medicare Part B deductible.

Type of Surgery : _____

_____

_____

_____

Estimated Charge for Surgery $ _____

Estimated Medicare Allowable Charge $ _____

Your Estimated Out-of-Pocket Expense $ _____

_____
Patient Signature   Date

Exhibit 4.12   Medicare Advanced Notice Service Waiver

Physician's Notice

Medicare will only pay for services that it determines to be "reasonable and necessary" under Section 1862(a)(1) of the Medicare law. If Medicare determines that a particular service, although it would otherwise be covered, is "not reasonable and necessary" under Medicare program standards, Medicare will deny payment for that service. I believe that, in your case, Medicare is likely to deny payment for the following reasons:

_____

_____

Note: On the above line, a specific procedure code and description of procedure *must* be listed here before the beneficiary signs the form.

Medicare does not usually pay:

1. For this many treatments/shots/visits.

2. For this service/drug/vaccine.

3. Because the treatment has yet to be proven effective.

4. For this office visit unless it was emergency care.

5. For like services by more than one doctor during the same time period.

6. For such an extensive procedure.

7. For this equipment or lab test.

8. Because the treatment is considered by Medicare to be "not reasonable or necessary."

Beneficiary Agreement

I, _____, have been informed on this date_____ by my physician (and/or staff) that he believes that Medicare is likely to deny payment for the service(s) identified above for the reasons stated. If Medicare denies payment, I agree to be personally and fully responsible for payment of the service(s) rendered.

Further, I will pay for these services on this date, understanding that the physician will bill my insurance(s) on my behalf. If the above physician is paid by my insurance, I will receive a refund for the portion of the bill covered by my insurance less any portion of the payment that is deemed my responsibility.

_____   _____
Beneficiary Signature   Staff/Witness Signature

Exhibit 4.13   **Insurance Coverage Advanced Notice
Service Waiver**

Physician's Notice

Some health insurance plans will only pay for services that they determine to be "reasonable and necessary." If an insurance plan determines that a particular service, although it would otherwise be covered, is "not reasonable and necessary," the insurance plan may deny payment for that service.

I believe that, in your case, your health plan is likely to deny payment for _____

_____

Policyholder/Patient Agreement

I, _____, have been informed on this date _____ by my physician (and/or staff) that he believes that my health plan may deny payment for the service identified above for the reasons stated. If the health plan denies payment, I agree to be personally and fully responsible for payment of the service(s) rendered.

Further, I will pay for these services on this date, understanding that the physician will attempt to re-bill my insurance(s) on my behalf. If the above physician is paid by my insurance, I will receive a refund for the portion of the bill covered by my insurance less any portion of the payment that is deemed my responsibility.

_____   _____
Policyholder/Patient Signature   Staff/Witness Signature

Probably the most important section in insurance billing is the assignment of primary and secondary insurance plan status. This is vital to assuring proper coordination of benefits, clean claim processing, and appropriate reimbursement. To accomplish this, the data entry staff must understand coordination of benefit rules when more than one insurance plan is involved in a patient's account, and then translate that on the insurance data entry screen.

Be careful to place the correct numbers and letters in the respective fields for policy numbers, plan numbers, group numbers, authorization or precertification numbers, and extra insurance information such as accident-related data. Also be careful to fully review your insurance plan utility file before adding any new insurance plans to a patient file. Multiple insurance entries for a single insurance plan can easily complicate account follow-up and management.

Another data field includes the patient's "financial" or "account type," which defines the primary account type for management and reporting purposes. The patient's account type is sometimes classified as a primary payer type (that is, Medicare, Medicaid, BC/BS, commercial, insurance only, self-pay, etc.).

Capture of All Billable Services and Transaction Entry

Under fee-for-service, the traditional way to receive appropriate reimbursement is for the physician to report all pertinent services provided to the patient in the medical record and capture all billable services for transaction entry into the billing system.

We use the term "appropriate reimbursement" because under most systems, CPT coding drives expected reimbursement. Accurate coding and reporting all services provided is the pre-claim processing area that makes or breaks a successful billing office. Yet, even under managed care plans that reimburse primary-care physicians on a capitated rate, complete medical documentation and coding of all services rendered is just as important to review resource allocation and costs associated with care. Documentation is also used for physician productivity measurements that determine profit sharing and continuity as a plan provider.

To successfully capture all billable services, the following areas need to be addressed:

1. **Comprehensive Medical Record Documentation**
   The medical record, while a clinical document, is also the ultimate medical billing document and is used by most health plans in adjudicating claims to support or deny reimbursements. Therefore, physicians need to develop

detailed and qualitative notes of patient evaluation and management (E/M) encounters, diagnostic and therapeutic treatments, supplies, orders, and so on.

In December 1994, the AMA and HCFA jointly distributed *New E/M Documentation Guidelines*, which thoroughly defines all documentation components needed to meet and exceed level of service definition criteria. All practices should have received a copy of the guidelines from their Medicare carrier and should request a copy if not received. In 1997 new E/M guidelines were distributed; however, these revised guidelines have been delayed by HCFA. Until HCFA decides to implement them, the 1994 or 1997 criteria may be used, whichever is more appropriate for the provider.

2. **Transfer of Clinical/Treatment Information to Appropriate CPT and ICD-9-CM Codes**

   From the medical record all the physician services rendered and all medications and supplies provided need to be identified and coded. In addition, the patient's chief complaints, signs, symptoms, or qualified diagnosis(es) also need to be coded using valid ICD-9-CM codes.

   As coding serves as the basis for appropriate reimbursement, *the quality of the practice's coding skills is extremely important.* The coding staff should be encouraged to become certified procedural coders or become affiliated with associations that encourage certification and offer coding education programs. In-house code training systems are also helpful in fostering staff coding skills.

   Key areas for coding skills include E/M level of service differentiation, CPT procedure and surgery coding, use of modifiers, supply and injectable drug billing, and the coding's potential impact on reimbursement. To properly coordinate insurance plan benefits between different physicians treating different diagnostic conditions, the assignment of the most appropriate Level I and II HCPCS codes (services and supplies) and ICD-9-CM diagnostic codes is needed to submit a clean claim and receive appropriate reimbursement.

   To facilitate the charge capture process, most practices develop customized billing source documents called encounter forms to serve as internal charge forms.

Encounter Forms

Encounter forms, also referred to as charge tickets, are preprinted forms that list procedure codes and descriptions (and occasionally diagnostic codes) for services frequently rendered by the practice. The form also usually contains basic practice and patient information and serves as an internal charge form and patient invoice. It is usually prenumbered for internal controls.

The services and diagnoses are usually arranged by service classification—evaluation and management (E/M) services, injections, minor procedures, diagnostic tests, laboratory, and radiology services. Some forms are printed on two-ply carbonless paper—one copy for the practice, the other to serve as the patient's receipt. Others are printed with sequential numbers for tracking purposes. A sample encounter form is shown in Chapter 1 (Exhibit 1.2).

Many practices rely on encounter forms because they are convenient. At the time of the visit, the physician or medical assistant simply checks off the services and patient diagnoses, the staff completes the charge information, and the charges are entered into the patient billing system. Unless required to file a claim, as in the case of Medicare, a copy of the encounter form is provided to the patient to file with his or her insurance claim. In addition to their convenience, encounter forms save time, can be used with many third-party payers, and simplify paperwork and bookkeeping.

Encounter forms do, however, have significant drawbacks. First, it is impossible to list on the encounter form the complete range of procedure and diagnosis codes that are likely to be used by your practice. This can lead to miscoding of services and diagnoses, as most practices inappropriately select the closest code rather than take the time to refer to the code manual to locate the correct code. Second, encounter forms cannot be submitted to Medicare, nor are they useful when submitting claims for nonroutine or unusual services.

Finally, encounter forms are most often used with patients who pay at the time of the visit. Because the patient files his or her own claim, you may not know if the claim was denied or delayed because of improper codes listed on the encounter form. This lack of feedback can increase coding and other encounter form errors, which result in underpayments to patients and audit liability to physician practices.

The final assignment of the HCPCS and ICD-9-CM codes on the encounter form is often a "shared" responsibility between the physician, clinical support staff, and business office support staff. The physician knows best what service and supplies were provided to a patient and what was documented. Unfortunately, the majority of physicians are not fond of coding, and some want to be totally free from the coding process. So, often the clinical support staff assists physicians in the assignment of HCPCS and ICD-9-CM codes. It is important to remember that in cases of improper coding on fraudulent claims, the ultimate responsibility lies with the provider whose signature is on the claim.

Service Verification and Transaction Entry of Services Rendered   After the services and diagnoses have been marked on the encounter form, the encounter form is brought to the cashiering-discharge area. This is where the encounter form is first reviewed as a quality assurance check by the clinical assistant and the in-office coding staff. They are responsible for:

- Reviewing the encounter form for complete charge capture and code assignment. They review the patient's chart against the encounter form for all supplies, drugs, and services provided

- Proper assignment of E/M type of service (for example, is the patient a new or established patient? Is an encounter an office visit or a consultation?)

- The compatibility of the ICD-9-CM codes with each CPT procedure code or E/M level of service

- Assigning the ICD-9-CM codes with fourth and fifth digits or to the highest specificity

When the coding staff is satisfied with the code assignment, the patient's account is pulled up on the transaction entry screen of the computer system. Again, most billing management systems have standardized data fields for transaction entry and correspond to the HCFA-1500 claim form (to be discussed later).

The key data fields to complete *per charge line item* include the following:

- Date of service (DOS)—sometimes defined as "from and to dates"

- Place of service code—for example, code 11=office, 21=hospital inpatient, 22=hospital outpatient

- Transaction codes—Level I (CPT) and Level II (HCPCS) codes

- Coding modifiers

- Attending practice physician code—defaults provider ID number

- Standard charge amount or special insurance charge default

- Number of units

- Definition of one to four diagnoses using ICD-9-CM codes

- Assignment of diagnosis codes to individual line items (one to four) cross-reference

The last data field for transaction entry on most billing systems is for indicating that the line item is to be billed to insurance. Some systems ask "bill insurance?" with a "Yes/No" field, while other systems allow the operator to bill a specific insurance plan through the assignment of insurance codes. After all line items have been coded, the transaction charges are added to the patient's account, and the patient's account is flagged by the system for generating a claim.

Filing Claims and Effect on Accounts Receivable

In the interest of keeping accounts receivable low, it is best to obtain payment from the patient at the time of service. However, most physicians file insurance claims on behalf of and for the circumstances in which patients are clearly incapable of filing claims, when the law requires the office to file the claim, or when patients forget to bring their checkbooks or credit cards or have no other way of making a payment. Remember, billed services become accounts receivable; it is always preferable to receive payment immediately.

To reemphasize the point, *the reason to avoid filing commercial insurance claims is to maximize cash flow.* If an insurance claim is filed for commercial insurance, it becomes an account receivable to the practice and thus is subject to all the office policies and procedures necessary to obtain payment from the insurance company.

If the office collects payment for the visit, there is no account receivable for that transaction. The more money the office can collect at the front desk, the better the practice cash flow will be. The front desk should be able to collect some payment for at least 90 percent of visits, even if a patient pays only $5. In some instances practices use charge cards to enhance collections and file the insurance for the patient. Although in many cases it is not mandatory for the practice to file the insurance claim, timing and proper filing of the form are enhanced when the practice completes the form.

Insurance Claims Processing and Submission

If a patient does not pay for the visit at the time of service, the office will need to prepare and file an insurance claim form with the patient's insurance company to receive payment. The manner in which the insurance claim form is completed and submitted will depend on the type of insurance. As was discussed before, some insurance companies only process paper claims, while others accept electronically submitted claims. So part of the insurance processing manager's responsibility is to organize which insurance claims need to be generated on paper and which can be sent electronically.

To receive appropriate payment from the insurance company, the office must prepare the insurance claim correctly, referred to as a "clean claim." This means that every relevant box must be completed on the claim form for the insurance plan to process. Any error in the claim completion may cause payment to be delayed or denied. The most common form used to file insurance claims is the type mandated for use for Medicare claims, the HCFA-1500 form.

HCFA-1500 Universal Claim Form

The HCFA-1500 form is often called the universal claim form because virtually all third-party payers will accept it. In 1992 the HCFA-1500 form was changed so that it can be scanned by payers using optical character recognition (OCR) equipment. As previously stated, Medicare requires that all physicians submit this form when providing services to Medicare patients.

In addition to using a special red ink for OCR purposes, the form was redesigned to allow for the reporting of additional information, such as the physician's unique physician identification number (UPIN), which is required by Medicare. These forms may be obtained from a variety of vendors and are relatively inexpensive. See Chapter 1.

Instructions for Completing a HCFA-1500 Form

Most insurance and managed care plans provide basic instructions for completing items on the claim form in the physician manual. If there are no special requirements, the item should be completed according to the requirements stated on the form. If the claim forms are not computer generated, it is best to type them. If they are handwritten, the staff should print the requirements using all capitals and black ink.

The claim form is divided into two major sections: patient information, items 1through 13, and physician information, items 14 through 33. Refer to Exhibit 1.1 to see a HCFA-1500 form in its entirety.

Patient and Insured Information   Items 1 through 13 ask for information about the patient and the insured, and for a determination of whether the patient is a dependent. This is information that was completed on the registration form at the patient's initial office visit or at the hospital.

In practices that use computerized patient information-accounting systems, this information can be generated automatically by entering a single patient identification number assigned by the practice.

The following sections describe each of these 13 items; below the general explanation, where applicable, there are descriptions of the special requirements for Medicare, Medicaid, CHAMPUS, CHAMPVA, and private plans.

Item 1: Type of Insurance

Indicate the type of insurance coverage applicable to a claim by checking the appropriate box. For example, if a Medicare claim is being submitted, check the Medicare box; for the Federal Employment Compensation Act/Black Lung, check FECA. For private plans, such as a Blue Shield claim, check OTHER.

Item 1a: Insured's ID Number

Enter the insured's primary identification number, including all letters. This is the number that appears on the plan identification card.

Medicare Enter the Health Insurance Claim Number (HICN) from the Medicare card, including all the letters.

Medicaid Enter the Medicaid number from the current Medicaid card. It is sometimes called the billing number or recipient number.

CHAMPUS Enter the sponsor's Social Security number (SSN). Do not provide the patient's SSN unless the patient and sponsor are the same. If a sponsor is an active-duty security agent, enter "SECURITY." Additional information about sponsors is given in Chapter 2.

CHAMPVA Provide the sponsor's SSN; add the number in item 5 of the CHAMPVA authorization card if there is no SSN.

Private Plans Enter the insured's subscriber, enrollee, or member number. This may be the certificate number of the insured, and it is copied directly from the plan's identification number. Frequently, this number is the insured's SSN.

Item 2: Patient's Name

Enter the patient's last name, first name, and middle initial, if any, as shown on the identification card. The practice may know the patient by a nickname or the individual may want to be known by his or her middle name, but enter the name exactly as it appears on the card.

Item 3: Patient's Birth Date

Enter the patient's birth date and sex. Because many plans operate under different rules, providers will want to contact individual payers who they do business with to determine how that payer is handling date formats.

Medicare Providers of services are required as of October 1, 1998 to report eight-digit birth dates for items 3, 9b, and 11a on HCFA-1500. This includes entering two-digit months (MM) and days (DD) and four-digit years (CCYY). The reporting requirement of eight-digit birthdates will not require a revision to HCFA-1500. Eight-digit birthdates must be reported with a space between month, day, and year (that is, MM\DD\CCYY). For example, if a patient's birthday is February 3, 1951, then the correct way to enter this date is 02 03 1951. On the HCFA-1500, the space between month, day, and year is delineated by a dotted, vertical line.

Item 4: *Insured's Name*

Enter the full name of the insured.

Medicare If there is a plan primary to Medicare, through the patient's or spouse's employment or any other source, list the name of the insured on that policy. When the insured and the patient are the same, enter the word "SAME." If Medicare is primary, leave blank.

Medicaid Enter the full name of the insured.

Private Plans Enter the full name of the insured if it is different from that of the patient.

Item 5: *Patient's Address*

Enter the patient's mailing address on the first line, the city and state on the second line, and the zip code and telephone number on the third line.

CHAMPUS Do not provide a post office box number—enter the actual place of residence. If this is a rural address, the address must contain the route and box number. An A.P.O./F.P.O. address should not be used for a patient's mailing address unless that person is actually residing overseas.

Item 6: *Patient Relationship to Insured*

Check the appropriate box for the patient's relationship to the insured after item 4 has been completed.

Medicare Enter the relationship of the individual whose coverage is the primary plan for the Medicare beneficiary.

CHAMPUS If the patient is the sponsor, check the "self" block. If "other" is checked, indicate how the patient is related to the sponsor, for example, former spouse, parent. Parents, parents-in-law, stepparents, and parents by adoption are not CHAMPUS/ CHAMPVA eligible. These categories of dependents may have ID cards with privileges for the military treatment facility, but not for CHAMPUS/CHAMPVA benefits. Grandchildren are not eligible unless they are legally adopted. Be certain that an ID card authorizes "CIVILIAN" medical benefits. Review the reverse side of the retiree's ID card (DD Form 2. Retired). An unnumbered block provides a date when civilian military care is no longer authorized, for example, when the CHAMPUS beneficiary becomes eligible for Medicare. If the child is a stepchild, check the "child" box.

Private Plans If the patient is the insured, check "self."

Item 7: Insured's Address

Enter the insured's address and telephone number. When this address is the same as the patient's address, enter the word "same." Complete this item only when items 4 and 11 have been completed.

CHAMPUS Enter the address for the active duty sponsor's duty station or the retiree's mailing address. If the address is the same as the patient's address, enter "same." If the sponsor resides overseas, enter the A.P.O./F.P.O. address.

Private Plans If the insured is the patient, enter "same."

Item 8: Patient Status

Check the appropriate box for the patient's marital status and indicate whether the patient is employed or is a full-time or part-time student.

Item 9: Other Insured's Policy or Group Number

Enter the insured's last name and first name for a plan that is secondary to the patient's primary insurance plan listed in item 2.

Medicare Enter the last name, first name, and middle initial of the enrollee in a Medigap policy if it is different from that shown in item 2. Otherwise, enter "same" or enrollee's name. If no Medigap benefits are assigned, leave this space blank.

Note: Only participating physicians are to complete items 9 and 9a-d and only when the beneficiary wishes to assign benefits under a Medigap policy.

Participating physicians and suppliers must enter the information required in item 9 and its divisions if this is requested by the beneficiary. A claim for which a beneficiary elects to assign benefits under a Medigap policy to a participating physician/supplier is called a *mandated Medigap transfer or crossover*.

Do not list other supplemental coverages that are not Medigap policies in item 9a-d when a Medicare claim is submitted. Other supplemental claims are forwarded automatically if the private plan contracts with a Medicare carrier to send Medicare claim information electronically. If there is no such contract, the beneficiary must file his or her own supplemental claim.

Medigap is medical insurance offered by a private plan to individuals covered by Medicare and is designed to supplement Medicare benefits. It fills in some of the gaps in Medicare coverage by providing payment for charges that Medicare does not cover, such as deductibles, coinsurance, and other limitations imposed by Medicare. It does not include limited benefit coverage available to Medicare beneficiaries such as a "specific disease," for example, cancer, or "hospital indemnity" per day coverage. Medigap excludes policies offered by an employer to employees or former employees, as well as policies offered by a labor union to members or former members.

CHAMPUS Enter the name of the insured if it is different from that shown in item 2 (patient). For example, the patient may be covered under a plan held by a spouse, parent, or other person. (Item 11a-d should be used to report insurance plans covering the patient.) **Note:** Item 11d should be completed before the office staff determines the need for completing items 9a-d. If item 11d is checked, items 9a-d must be completed.

Private Plans Enter the name of the insured for secondary insurance plans to the patient's primary plan listed in item 2.

Item 9a: Other Insured's Policy or Group Number

Enter the plan ID number, which is the policy or group number of the secondary insurance plan.

Medicare Enter the policy and/or group number of the Medigap insured preceded by MEDIGAP, MG, or MGAP. **Note:** Item 9d must be completed if you enter a policy and/or group number in item 9a.

CHAMPUS Enter the policy number of the other insured's plan.

Private Plans List the policy number of the secondary plan.

Item 9b: Other Insured's Date of Birth

Medicare Enter the Medigap insured's eight-digit birth date (MM\DD\CCYY) and sex. Because many plans operate under different rules, providers will want to contact individual payers who they do business with to determine how that payer is handling date formats.

Item 9c: Employer's Name or School Name

Enter the employer's name or school name for the secondary insurance plan.

Medicare Leave blank if a Medigap PAYERID is entered in item 9d. Enter the claims-processing address for the Medigap insurer. Use an abbreviated street address, two-letter state postal code, and zip code copied from the Medigap enrollee's Medigap identification card. For example,

1257 Anywhere Street
Baltimore, MD 21204

is shown as

1257 Anywhere St. MD 21204.

CHAMPUS Enter the name of the employer or school.

Item 9d: Insurance Plan Name or Program Name

Enter the name of the insurance program or plan that received the claim after the plan noted in item 1.

Medicare Enter the nine-digit PAYERID number of the Medigap insurer. If no PAYERID number exists, then enter the Medigap insurance program or plan name. If you are a participating provider and the beneficiary wants Medicare payment data forwarded to a Medigap insurer under a mandated Medigap transfer, all of the information in items 9, 9a, 9b, and 9d must be complete and accurate. Otherwise, the Medicare carrier cannot forward the claim information to the Medigap insurer.

CHAMPUS Enter the name of the insurance plan or the program name where the individual has other health insurance benefits. On an attached sheet, provide a complete mailing address for all other insurance information and enter the word "attachment."

Item 10: Is Patient Condition Related to:

If the services listed on the claim form are for a work-related injury or accident-related injury, check the "yes" box.

Medicare Check "yes" or "no" to indicate whether employment, auto liability, or other accident involvement applies to one or more of the services described in item 24. Any item checked "yes" indicates that there may be subrogation primary to Medicare. Identify primary insurance information in item 11.

CHAMPUS Check "yes" or "no," but if this service was the result of an automobile accident, indicate the state where the accident occurred. The contractor will contact the patient for potential third-party liability information. When a third-party liability is involved, the beneficiary is required to complete DD Form 2527, Statement of Personal Injury—Possible Third-Party Liability.

Private Plans Provide information concerning potential third-party liability.

Item 10d: Reserved for Local Use

Medicaid If the patient is entitled to Medicaid, enter the patient's number preceded by the letters MCD.

CHAMPUS Use this block to indicate that there is other health insurance.

Item 11: Insured's Policy Group or FECA Number

Enter the insured's policy group or FECA number. If it is the same as in item 4, write "same."

Medicare THIS ITEM MUST BE COMPLETED BY THE PHYSICIAN, *who acknowledges having made a good faith effort to determine whether Medicare is the primary or secondary plan.* If there is insurance primary to Medicare, enter the insured's plan ID number and complete items 11a-c. If there is no insurance primary to Medicare, enter the word "none."

Medicare payment may be secondary to other insurance under the following circumstances:

- Group health plan coverage
  - Working aged
  - Disability
  - End-stage renal disease
- No-fault and/or other liability
- Work-related illness/injury
  - Workers' compensation
  - Black lung
  - Veterans benefits

Note: For a paper claim to be considered for Medicare secondary payer benefits, a copy of the primary payer EOB must be forwarded along with the claim form.

CHAMPUS If the patient has other insurance, enter the plan ID number and indicate whether the patient is covered by Medicare. (Block 9a-d should be used to report another primary insurance plan.)

Item 11a: Insured's Date of Birth

Enter the insured's eight-digit (MM\DD\CCYY) birth date and sex if they are different from those in item 3.

CHAMPUS Complete the insured's eight-digit date of birth (MM\DD\CCYY) and sex (check box). Enter the date of birth and sex if they are different from those in item 3.

Item 11b: Employer's Name or School Name

Medicare Enter the employer's name, if applicable. If there is a change in the insured's insurance status, for example, retired, enter either a six-digit (MM\DD\YY) or eight-digit (MM\DD\CCYY) retirement date preceded by the word "retired."

CHAMPUS Enter the employer's or school's name if applicable.

Item 11c: Insurance Plan Name or Program Name

Enter the nine-digit PAYERID number of the primary insurer. If no PAYERID number exists, then enter the complete primary insurance plan or program name, such as Blue Shield of Illinois. If the primary payer's EOB does not contain the claims processing address, record the primary payer's claims processing address directly on the EOB.

CHAMPUS Enter the insurance plan or program name. If the patient has supplemental CHAMPUS coverage, it is not necessary to report a claim with that insurance first unless the insurance can be considered a primary plan. For CHAMPUS purposes, supplemental policies are those that are specifically designed to supplement CHAMPUS benefits, for example, payment of the beneficiary's cost share or deductible liability. Remember, CHAMPUS is secondary to all other medical insurance except Medicaid. When you submit the claim to the other insurer, attach a copy of the EOB from the primary insurance plan to the CHAMPUS claim.

Item 11d: Is There Another Health Benefit Plan?

Medicare Leave blank. Not required by Medicare.

CHAMPUS Check "yes" or "no" to indicate that there is or is not another primary insurance plan. If the patient is covered by secondary insurance, Medicare, or Medicaid, enter that plan ID number. If the patient is covered by Medicaid, enter the word "Medicaid," followed by the Medicaid number.

Private Plans Place an X in the "yes" box to indicate patient coverage by a third insurance plan. Enter the group number or group name if the patient is covered by an employer-paid medical insurance plan.

Item 12: Patient's or Authorized Person's Signature

The patient or authorized representative must sign and enter either a six-digit date (MM\DD\YY), eight-digit date (MM\DD\CCYY), or an alphanumeric date (for example, January 1, 1998) unless the signature is on file. The patient or authorized representative must sign the item unless the signature is on file in the practice or at the hospital. The signed authorization for the patient that is on file at the hospital should cover all inpatient and outpatient hospitalization services related to the services on the claim form. When the patient's representative signs, the relationship to the patient must be indicated. The patient's signature, authorizing the release of medical information, is necessary to process the claim. The patient's signature also authorizes payment of benefits to the provider of service when the provider accepts assignment on the claim.

Medicare The program allows the obtaining of a lifetime authorization one time, which is kept on file. The registration form in Chapter 2 contains the terminology required by Medicare, and so a separate authorization is not necessary if the form is used. If a signature is obtained, enter "Signature on File" in item 12.

Signature by Mark (X). When an illiterate or physically handicapped patient signs by mark, the patient's name and address must be entered next to the mark.

CHAMPUS If a patient is under 18 years of age, either parent should sign unless the services are confidential. If the patient is 18 or older, but cannot sign the claim, the person who signs must be either the legal guardian or, in the absence of a legal guardian, the spouse or parent of the patient. The signer should write the patient's name in item 12, followed by the word "by" and his or her own signature. A statement must be attached to the claim giving the signer's full name and address, the signer's relationship to the patient, and the reason the patient is unable to sign. Also included must be documentation of the signer's appointment as a legal guardian, an indication of whether a power of attorney has been issued, or a statement that a legal guardian has not been appointed if such is the case.

Private Plans It is very important to maintain current signatures for patients and/or insureds. Use the words "signature on file" if a valid signature is available. Most insurance and managed care plans will accept this, but have the right to request a copy of the actual signature.

Item 13: Insured's or Authorized Person's Signature

The signature in this item authorizes payment of medical benefits to the physician or provider for services listed on the claim.

Medicare The signature in this item authorizes payment of mandated Medigap benefits to the participating physician or supplier if required Medigap information is included in item 9 and its subdivisions. The patient or his/her authorized representative signs this item, or the signature must be on file as a separate Medigap authorization. The Medigap assignment on file in the participating provider's office must be insurer specific. It may state that the authorization applies to all occasions of service until it is revoked.

Private Plans If a plan has offered a contract for participation in its program and the physician has not signed the contract, even though the signature is in item 13, payment may not be sent to the practice.

Physician or Supplier Information These items describe diagnoses, procedures, and charges and give a history of the patient's condition. Most of this information is found on the patient's encounter form.

Item 14: Date of Current Illness, Injury, Pregnancy
Enter either a six-digit (MM\DD\YY) or eight-digit (MM\DD\CCYY) date when the first symptoms began for the current illness, injury, or pregnancy (date of last menstrual period).

Medicare For chiropractic services, enter either a six-digit (MM\DD\YY) or eight-digit (MM\DD\CCYY) date of the initiation of the course of treatment and then enter either a six-digit (MM\DD\YY) or eight-digit (MM\DD\CCYY) x-ray date in item 19.

Private Plans This information is used in determining benefits or exclusions for preexisting conditions.

Item 15: If Patient Has Had Same or Similar Illness

Medicare Leave blank.

CHAMPUS Enter the date when the patient first consulted the physician for a similar condition.

Private Plans Enter the date when the patient first consulted the physician for a similar condition.

Item 16: Dates Patient Unable to Work in Current Occupation
Enter the dates the patient is employed and unable to work in his or her current occupation. Enter either six-digit (MM\DD\YY) or eight-digit (MM\DD\CCYY) dates when the patient is unable to work. This is important if the patient has employment-related insurance coverage or workers' compensation.

Item 17: Name of the Referring Physician or Other Source
Medicare Enter the name of the referring or ordering physician if the service or item was ordered or referred by a physician.

A *referring physician* is a physician who requests an item or service for the beneficiary for which payment may be made under the Medicare program. An *ordering physician* is a physician who orders nonphysician services for the patient, such as diagnostic laboratory tests, clinical laboratory tests, pharmaceutical services, and durable medical equipment.

The ordering/referring requirement became effective on January 1, 1992. *All* claims for Medicare covered services and items that result from a physician's order or referral must include the ordering/referring physician's name and *national provider identifier* (NPI). An NPI is a unique number assigned to each physician or other practitioner who bills the Medicare program. This includes parenteral and enteral nutrition, immunosuppressive drug claims, and the following:

- Diagnostic laboratory services
- Diagnostic radiology services
- Consultative services
- Durable medical equipment

Claims for other ordered/referred services that are not included in the preceding list must also show the ordering or referring physician's name and NPI. For example, a surgeon must complete items 17 and 17a when a physician sends a patient for a consultation. When the ordering physician is also the performing physician (as is often the case with in-office clinical laboratory tests), the performing physician's name and assigned NPI must appear in items 17 and 17a.

All physicians must obtain an NPI even though they may never bill Medicare directly. A physician who has not been assigned an NPI must contact the Medicare carrier. When a patient is referred to a physician who also orders and performs a diagnostic service, a separate claim is required for the diagnostic service.

- Enter the original ordering or referring physician's name and NPI in items 17 and 17a of the first claim form.
- Enter the ordering (performing) physician's name and NPI in items 17 and 17a of the second claim form.

CHAMPUS Provide the name and address of the physician, institutional provider, or other source who referred the patient to the provider of the services identified on this claim. This is required for all consultation services. If your patient was referred from a military treatment facility (MTF), enter the name of the MTF and attach part DD2161 of SF 513, "Referral."

Item 17a: *ID Number of Referring Physician*
Medicare Enter the HCFA-assigned NPI of the referring or ordering physician listed in item 17. Enter only the seven-digit base number and the one-digit check digit.

When a claim involves multiple referring or ordering physicians, a separate HCFA-1500 must be used for each ordering or referring physician.

If the ordering or referring physician has not been assigned an NPI , one of the *surrogate* NPIs listed below must be used in item 17a. The surrogate NPI that is used depends on the circumstance. Enter the physician's name in item 17 and the surrogate NPI in item 17a. All surrogate NPIs, with the exception of retired physicians (RET000), are temporary and may be used only until an NPI is assigned.

- Use the following surrogate NPIs for physicians who have not been assigned individual NPIs. Claims received with surrogate numbers will be tracked and may be audited.

- Residents who are issued an NPI in conjunction with activities outside their residency status must use that NPI. For interns and residents without NPIs, use the eight-character surrogate NPI RES00000.

- Retired physicians who were not issued an NPI may use the surrogate RET00000.

- Physicians serving in the Department of Veteran Affairs or the U.S. Armed Services may use VAD00000.

- Physicians serving in the Public Health or Indian Health Services may use PHS00000.

Medicare extends coverage and direct payment in certain areas to practitioners who are state licensed to order medical services including diagnostic tests or to refer patients to Medicare providers without a supervising physician. Use the surrogate NPI NPP00000 on claims involving services ordered or referred by nurse practitioners, clinical nurse specialists, or any nonphysician practitioner who is state licensed to order clinical diagnostic tests.

When the ordering or referring physician has not been assigned an NPI and does not qualify to use one of the surrogate NPIs, use the surrogate NPI OTH00000 until an individual NPI is assigned.

Item 18: *Hospitalization Dates Related to Current Services*
Enter either a six-digit (MM\DD\YY) or an eight-digit (MM\DD\CCYY) date when a medical service is furnished as a result of, or subsequent to, a related hospitalization.

Item 19: *Reserved for Local Use*
Medicare Enter either a six-digit (MM\DD\YY) or an eight-digit (MM\DD\CCYY) date patient was last seen and the NPI of his/her attending

physician when an independent physical or occupational therapist or physician providing routine foot care submits claims. For physical and occupational therapists, entering this information certifies that the required physician certification (or recertification) is being kept on file.

Enter either a six-digit (MM\DD\YY) or an eight-digit (MM\DD\CCYY) x-ray date for chiropractor services. By entering an x-ray date and the initiation date for course of chiropractic treatment in item 14, you are certifying that all the relevant information requirements (including level of subluxation) are on file along with the appropriate x-ray and all are available for carrier review.

Enter the drug's name and dosage when submitting a claim for not otherwise classified (NOC) drugs.

Enter a concise description of an "unlisted procedure code" or an NOC code if one can be given within the confines of this box. Otherwise, an attachment must be submitted with the claim.

Enter all applicable modifiers when modifier -99 (multiple modifiers) is entered in item 24d. If modifier -99 is entered on multiple line items of a single claim form, all applicable modifiers for each line item containing a -99 modifier should be listed as follows: 1=(mod), where the number 1 represents the line item and "mod" represents all modifiers applicable to the referenced line item.

Enter the statement "Homebound" when an independent laboratory renders an electrocardiogram tracing or obtains a specimen from a homebound or institutionalized patient.

Enter the statement "Patient refuses to assign benefits" when the beneficiary absolutely refuses to assign benefits to a participating provider. In this case, no payment may be made on the claim.

Enter the statement "Testing for hearing aid" when billing for services involving the testing of a hearing aid(s) is used to obtain intentional denials when other payers are involved.

When dental examinations are billed, enter the specific surgery for which the exam is being performed.

Enter the specific name and dosage amount when low osmolar contrast material is billed, but only if HCPCS codes do not cover them.

Enter either a six-digit (MM\DD\YY) or eight-digit (MM\DD\CCYY) assumed and/or relinquished date for a global surgery claim when providers share postoperative care.

Enter the statement "Attending physician, not hospice employee" when a physician renders services to a hospice patient but the hospice providing the patient's care (in which the patient resides) does not employ the attending physician.

Enter demonstration ID number "30" for all national emphysema treatment trial claims.

Item 20: Outside Lab

Medicare Complete this item when billing for diagnostic tests subject to purchase price limitations. A "yes" check indicates that the diagnostic test was performed outside the entity billing for the service. When "yes" is annotated, item 32 must be completed. Enter the purchase price under charges (item 24f) if the "yes" block is marked. A "no" check indicates that "no purchased tests are included on this claim." When billing for multiple purchased diagnostic tests, each test must be submitted on a separate claim form.

Private Plans Leave blank unless instructions are given by a specific plan.

Item 21: Diagnosis or Nature of Illness or Injury

Enter the patient's diagnosis and/or condition by using ICD-9-CM code numbers. Enter up to four codes in priority orders (primary condition, secondary condition, comorbid conditions, and complications). All narrative diagnoses for nonphysician specialties must be submitted on an attachment.

Item 22: Medicaid Resubmissions

Leave this blank. It is required by some Medicaid agencies if the agency is going to resubmit a claim. Show the resubmission code and the original claim reference number.

Item 23: Prior Authorization Number

Enter the professional review organization (PRO) prior authorization number for those procedures requiring PRO prior approval.

Enter the investigational device exemption (IDE) number when an investigational device is used in an FDA-approved clinical trial.

For physicians performing care plan oversight services, enter the six-digit Medicare provider number of the home health agency (HHA) or hospice when CPT code 99375 or 99376 or HCPCS code G0064, G0065, or G0066 is billed.

Enter the ten-digit CLIA (Clinical Laboratory Improvement Act) certification number for laboratory services billed by a physician office laboratory.

CHAMPUS Attach a copy of the authorization, for example, mental health preauthorization, heart-hung transplant authorization.

Private Plans If required, enter the preauthorization number.

Item 24a: Dates of Service

Enter either the six-digit (MM\DD\YY) or eight-digit (MM\DD\CCYY) date for each procedure, service, or supply. When "from" and "to" are shown for a series of identical services, enter the number of days or units in column 24g.

Item 24b: Place of Service

There are variations in the codes used for place of service (POS). The previous HCFA form (1-84) had specific codes printed on the reverse side for use in column 24b. HCFA (12-90) has no such codes printed. Some insurance plans still require the old (1-84) POS codes, and many require the new (12-90) ones.

Medicare Use the new POS codes. Identify the location, using a POS code, for each item used or service performed.

Note: When a service is rendered to a hospital inpatient, use the "inpatient hospital" code.

CHAMPUS Use the new POS codes.

Private Plans Check with the plan's billing instructions to determine which POS codes are required.

Item 24c: Type of Service

The type of service code is listed here when this is required.

Medicare Providers are not required to complete this item.

Private Plans Some plans require the use of type of service codes. Otherwise, leave it blank.

Item 24d: Procedures, Services, Supplies

Enter the five-digit CPT code or the HCPCS Level II/III number for the service. Up to three modifiers can be used in the spaces next to the code. The first modifier is added between the solid line and the dotted line on the forms. If three modifiers are necessary, there should be two blank spaces between the second and third in the item to the right of the dotted line.

Medicare Enter the procedures, services, or supplies, using the HCPCS codes. When applicable, show the HCPCS modifier with any procedure code.

Enter the specific code without a narrative description. However, when reporting an "unlisted procedure code" or an NOC code, include a narrative description in item 19, if a coherent description can be given within the confines of that box. Otherwise, an attachment must be submitted with the claim.

Private Plans Not all modifiers are accepted. It is best to check with the individual plan to see which modifiers it recognizes.

Item 24e: Diagnosis Code

Enter the diagnosis code reference number as shown in item 21 to relate the date of service and the procedures performed to the appropriate diagnosis.

Medicare Enter only one reference number per line item. When multiple services are performed, enter the primary reference number for each service; either a 1, a 2, a 3, or a 4. If a situation arises where two or more diagnoses are required for a procedure code (for example, Pap smears), you must reference only one of the diagnoses in item 21.

Item 24f: $Charges

Enter the charges for each listed service.

Item 24g: Days or Units

Enter the number of days or units. This field is most commonly used for multiple visits, units of supplies, anesthesia minutes, or oxygen volume. If only one service is performed, the numeral 1 must be entered.

Some services require that the actual number or quantity provided be clearly indicated on the claim form as units of service (for example, multiple ostomy or urinary supplies, medication dosages, or allergy testing procedures). When multiple services are provided, enter the actual number provided.

For anesthesia services, show the elapsed time in minutes in item 24g. Convert hours into minutes and enter the total minutes required for this procedure.

Item 24h: EPSDT Family Plan

Medicare Leave blank. Not required by Medicare.

Medicaid Use a checkmark or X if preventive services were provided under Medicaid.

Item 24i: EMG (Emergency)

Medicare Leave blank. Not required by Medicare.

CHAMPUS It is best to mark this block to indicate that the service was provided in a hospital emergency room.

Private Plans Some plans may require that this item be marked to indicate the service was provided in a hospital emergency room.

Item 24j: COB (Coordination of Benefits)

Medicare Enter the NPI of the performing provider of service/supplier if they are a member of a group practice.

Note: Enter the first two digits of the NPI in item 24j. Enter the remaining six digits of the NPI in item 24k, including the two-digit location identifier.

When several different providers of service or suppliers within a group are billing on the same HCFA-1500, show the individual NPI in the corresponding line item.

Private Plans Check this item if the patient is covered by one or more private plans. These plans are identified in items 11 and 11a-d.

Item 24k: Reserved for Local Use

Medicare Enter the NPI of the performing provider of service/supplier if they are a member of a group practice.

Note: Enter the first two digits of the NPI in item 24j. Enter the remaining six digits of the NPI in item 24k, including the two-digit location identifier.

CHAMPUS Enter the state license number of the provider.

Private Plans Not required.

Item 25: Federal Tax ID Number

Enter the physician/supplier federal tax ID (employer identification number) or Social Security number.

Medicare The participating physician or supplier's federal tax ID number is required for a mandated Medigap transfer.

Item 26: Patient's Account No.

Enter the patient's account number that was assigned by the practice's accounting system. This is an optional way to enhance patient identification by the physician. Some private plans, Medicaid, and some Medicare carriers include this information on their EOBs. It is easier to identify the patients and post the payments. As a service, any account numbers entered here will be returned to you.

Item 27: Accept Assignment?

Medicare Check the appropriate box to indicate whether the physician accepts assignment of benefits. If Medigap is indicated in item 9 and Medigap payment authorization is given in item 13, the physician must also be a

Medicare participating physician and must accept assignment of Medicare benefits for all covered charges for all patients.

The following services can be paid only on an assignment basis:

- Clinical diagnostic laboratory services
- Physician services provided to individuals entitled to both Medicare and Medicaid
- Participating physician/supplier services
- Services of physician assistants, nurse practitioners, clinical nurse specialists, nurse midwives, certified registered nurse anesthetists, clinical psychologists, and clinical social workers
- Ambulatory surgical center services for covered ASC procedures
- Home dialysis supplies and equipment paid under Method II

CHAMPUS Check "yes" if you accept assignment—check "no" if you do not. Failure to complete this block results in nonacceptance of assignment. "Accept assignment" means that the provider has agreed to be a CHAMPUS participating provider on the claim and will accept the allowable amount as the total amount payable. When a provider accepts assignment, payment will be made to the provider. If the provider does not accept assignment, payment will be made to the patient or sponsor.

Private Plans Not applicable to plans with which the physician has a contract.

Item 28: Total Charge

Enter total charges for the services reported on the claim (that is, the total of all charges in item 24f).

Item 29: Amount Paid

Enter the total amount the patient paid on the covered services only.

CHAMPUS Enter the amount received by the provider or supplier from the other plans or insurances. If the amount includes payment by any other insurance, the other insurance EOB, worksheet, or denial showing the amounts paid or denied must be attached to the CHAMPUS claim. Payment from the beneficiary should not be included.

Item 30: Balance Due

Enter the balance due (item 28 minus item 29).

Medicare Leave blank—not required by Medicare.

Item 31: *Signature of Physician or Supplier Including Degrees or Credentials*

Enter the signature of the physician and/or his or her representative and either the six-digit (MM\DD\YY), eight-digit (MM\DD\CCYY), or alphanumeric date (for example, January 1, 1998) the form was signed.

CHAMPUS The signature of physician or supplier, including degree(s) or credentials and the date of the signature, is necessary unless other authorized signatures are on file with the contractor.

Item 32: *Name and Address of Facility Where Services Were Rendered (If Other Than Home or Office)*

Enter the name and address of the facility if services were furnished in a hospital, clinic, laboratory, or facility other than the patient's home or the physician's office.

Medicare When the name and address of the facility where the services were furnished is the same as the biller's name and address shown in item 33, enter the word "SAME." Providers of service (namely physicians) must identify the supplier's name, address, and NPI when billing for purchased diagnostic tests. When more than one supplier is used, a separate HCFA-1500 should be used to bill each supplier.

This item is completed whether the supplier personnel performed the work at the physician's office or at another location.

If a QB or QU modifier is billed, indicating that the service was rendered in a health professional shortage area (HPSA), the physical location where the service was rendered must be entered if other than home. However, if the address shown in item 33 is in an HPSA and is the same as where the services were rendered, enter the word "SAME."

If the supplier is a certified mammography screening center, enter the six-digit FDA-approved certification number.

Complete this item for all laboratory work performed outside a physician's office. If an independent laboratory is billing, enter the place where the test was performed and the NPI, including the two-digit location identifier.

Item 33: *Physician's, Supplier's Billing Name, Address, Zip Code, and Telephone Number*

Enter the physician and/or supplier's billing name, address, zip code, and telephone number.

Medicare Enter the NPI, including the two-digit location identifier, for the performing physician who is *not* a member of a group practice. Enter the group NPI, including the two-digit location identifier, for the performing physician who *is* a member of a group practice.

CHAMPUS Enter the provider number.

Private Plans Enter the provider number for the plan.

Insurance Claim Processing Cycles

The number of claims generated will depend on the practice's volume of patients seen, type of services provided, and third-party payer mix. And, based on the volume of claims, each practice will need to determine its individual "insurance claim billing cycles." Some practices generate claims at the end of each day, while others process claims only once a week. Always keep in mind that the sooner a claim is generated and submitted, the faster the insurance plan is likely to process it.

Filing Primary Insurance Claims

Insurance claims must be filed for patients covered by Medicare, Medicaid, workers' compensation, and almost all managed care plans, as required by law or the plan's contract with the physician. A medical office generally files primary insurance claims for all services provided as a courtesy to the patient.

To generate a claim form for all of the patient accounts that have been flagged to be billed to insurance, the insurance processing manager bills by account number, insurance plan, or patient last name using "from" and "to" data fields to define the range of patients to be billed. The computer system then generates claims one after another for patients meeting the selection criteria.

Once generated, the forms are separated and organized by insurance company name and address. Again, the way the claims are selected will have a great impact on the amount of manual sorting the office staff will need to perform to get the claims mailed out.

Before mailing insurance claims, the office should make sure all forms from the patients required by insurance companies have been completed and mailed. For example, some insurance plans have their own authorization statements that must be signed by the patients and submitted to the insurance companies before the physicians can be paid. If patients were referred by other physicians within HMOs or PPOs, make sure the appropriate referral forms have been completed and mailed, if applicable. Many managed care plans require primary care physicians to complete physician referral forms when patients are referred to specialists. To be paid, the specialists' offices must attach these forms to their own insurance claims.

Filing Secondary Insurance Claims

Most medical practices also file secondary insurance claims for their patients. Secondary insurance policies generally cover the services or patient responsibilities not covered by primary insurance plans. In almost all cases, these types of policies act as a supplement to Medicare coverage. Medicare supplemental insurance, or a "Medigap" policy, is a health insurance plan designed specifically to supplement Medicare's benefits by filling in some of the gaps in Medicare coverage. Not all supplemental policies provide the same benefits. Some pay for the Medicare deductible, while most pay the co-insurance amount. Some policies even cover a limited number of services not covered under the Medicare program.

It is crucial for an office to detect when a patient has a supplemental policy. If it does not, the office will often receive payment from Medicare and bill the patient for the co-insurance or deductible. After waiting a period of time, the office finds out the patient has not paid because he or she thought the office was filing the secondary insurance claim. This activity puts a strain on a practice's cash flow and creates older accounts receivable. The new patient information form must include a section that indicates if a secondary insurance policy is in force. In addition, front-desk personnel should be trained always to ask the patient if he or she has a supplemental policy, whether the patient is new or established.

The most important aspect of filing a patient's secondary insurance is timeliness. Because secondary insurance claims are for a relatively small amount of money, many practices do not pay strict attention to filing them. This delays the office's reimbursement and impedes its cash flow. It could also create inefficiencies because the collection personnel will have to spend time collecting a large number of small-balance accounts.

Secondary insurance claims are submitted on the patient's behalf *only after notification is received from the primary insurance company* as to the claim's disposition (for example, payment in full, partial payment, denials, etc.). Usually within 30 days of claim receipt, insurance carriers send an explanation of benefits (EOB) along with the payment to explain the way the claim was processed.

An EOB is an accompaniment to the check from the insurance company that indicates the services submitted on the claim and how much of the charged amount for each service was:

- Approved for payment (that is, the allowance or allowable amount)
- Disallowed or contractually adjusted (that is, amount of allowance that is unrecoverable)
- Applied to the patient's annual deductible
- Applied to the patient's co-payment responsibilities
- Reduced or denied with explanation of determination
- Applied to other sources, such as "withhold" fees in managed care plans

EOBs provide the practice with essential information about the patient's financial responsibilities and the coordination of benefits between multiple insurance plans. A sample EOB is shown in Exhibit 4.14. While the actual EOB review process and payment posting will be discussed later, we will now finalize how to process secondary insurance claims.

After the primary insurance EOB data have been posted in the transaction entry payment screen, the practice processes all patient accounts with secondary insurance plans that continue to have an outstanding accounts receivable balance due. The billing system generates a claim that indicates the services provided and the amount paid by the other insurance plan. When submitting the secondary claim form, *always attach a copy of the patient's EOB from the primary insurance company*. The EOB assists the secondary payer in determining the coordination of benefits and ultimate patient responsibility.

Organizing Copies of Insurance Claim Forms

Depending on your billing system or whether your practice uses single-form or two-ply carbonless HCFA-1500 forms, the practice may need to file copies of the claim forms generated. Most practices file copies of unpaid insurance claim forms in a centralized location in the office so that anyone can go to that location and find the unpaid insurance claims. Centralizing the insurance claim forms allows for (a) easy access when performing insurance follow-up procedures, (b) a quick review of the claim forms if such a review is required, and (c) the easy tracing of the unpaid claims to other source documents in the office.

For example, the hard copies of the insurance claims should be traced to the computer-generated unpaid insurance report to ensure the report's accuracy. The hard copy of the insurance claims can be used to trace to the patient's ledger accounts for internal control purposes. In this situation, insurance claim

Exhibit 4.14   Explanation of Benefits

Participant Information:

Check #:	0123456789#
Participant:	Last, First
SS #:	987-65-4321
Group #:	00000

To assist us in serving you, please include participant information and patient's name when you direct inquiries to:

Claims Office
P.O. Box 00000
Anywhere, USA 00000
Telephone (999) 888-9999

Explanation of Benefits

For services provided by: Iwill Fixit, MD

Patient/ Service	Service Date(s)	(A) Total Charge	–	(B) Excluded Amounts	–	(C) Not Payable by Plan	–	(D) Co-insurance Amount %	=	(E) Plan Paid Amount %
Last, F										
Office visit	02/17/94	56.00		11.00 EM		10.00 CA				35.00 100%
X-ray	02/17/94	268.00				250.00 DD		3.60 20%		14.40 80%
Lab	02/17/94	20.00				15.00 CA				5.00 100%
Totals		**344.00**		**11.00**		**275.00**		**3.60**		**54.40**

Payments made to:
03/04/94   Iwill Fixit, MD $54.40

Codes and Remarks

EM: This amount represents the discount that resulted from the patient using a preferred provider. The patient is not responsible for this amount.

CA: This is the patient's copayment amount for this charge. The patient is responsible for this amount.

DD: This amount was applied to the patient's deductible.

amounts must always agree with the patient's accounts receivable on the account ledger.

One easy way to centralize the unpaid forms is to keep the office copies in an alphabetical or numerical expandable folder until payment is received. For insurance claims that are filed electronically, the electronic claim submission edit report, or a white paper printout of the actual insurance claim forms, should be maintained in the centralized file.

As practical as this sounds, it may prove impractical for some medical offices. This is especially true for practices that file a large number of claim forms and for offices that file most of their claims electronically. No matter how an office files its claims, an important practice management goal is to make sure all unpaid insurance claim forms are maintained in one centralized location.

Medicare Supplemental Insurance Policy Letters

Supplemental policies are separate health plans from another insurer that serve as a "secondary" source of coverage. Some supplemental insurance plans, referred to as "Medigap plans," are designed to supplement Medicare co-insurance, deductibles, and sometimes noncovered or unpaid services from Medicare. Many Medicare patients have these policies.

Supplemental plans are to be billed after Medicare has made its determination on a claim. In many states, the Medicare carrier will forward a claim to the supplemental carrier on behalf of the patient if the physician is participating with Medicare. This is commonly referred to as crossover claims processing.

In other states, the patient is responsible for filing the claim with the carrier for the supplemental policy. In some cases, the practice submits the claim on behalf of the patient; in other cases, the patient submits the claim.

If your practice does not accept assignment on Medicare claims and the patient has a supplemental policy, the following two sample letters (Exhibits 4.15 and 4.16) can be used to explain what the patient needs to do in each circumstance. Such letters can help to reduce the number of routine insurance calls to your office.

Deductible Letters

Often, patients are not sure whether they have met their annual deductible. The following letter can be used to inform patients about their deductible and the necessary payment they need to make to your practice. A sample letter is shown in Exhibit 4.17.

Exhibit 4.15   Sample Letter for Filling a Supplemental Claim When the *Practice* Will File the Claim

Dear Patient:

Supplemental policies are policies that pay for copayments, deductibles, and sometimes other services and procedures that are not paid by Medicare. They are billed for the part not paid for by your Medicare policy. This second billing may pay the majority, if not all, of the balance due our office after Medicare pays.

Should you have a supplemental insurance policy, we will be happy to submit a claim on your behalf once we receive your Explanation of Medicare Benefits and check. The Explanation of Medicare Benefits is the portion attached to your Medicare reimbursement check.

Any questions you have regarding payment of your claim should be directed to the Medicare office. Their toll-free number is 1-800-_____-_____, or you may call our office and speak with the billing supervisor.

After the supplemental policy has made a determination on the claim, we will notify you if there is a remaining balance due.

Thank you.

Sincerely,

[Name of Office Manager or Physician]

**Exhibit 4.16   Sample Letter for Filling a Supplemental Claim
When the *Patient* Will File the Claim**

Dear Patient:

As required by law, we have submitted your Medicare insurance form for services we provided to you recently. In addition, you will find enclosed a completed insurance claim form for your supplemental policy. Upon receiving payment from Medicare, attach the Explanation of Medicare Benefits to the enclosed claim form before mailing it to your insurance carrier for processing.

Please do not send the form to the supplemental insurance company until you have been paid by Medicare and have attached the Explanation of Medicare Benefits to the form. Submitting the enclosed claim form without the Explanation of Medicare Benefits attached will result in a denied or delayed claim.

We are happy to provide our patients with this service. If you have any questions regarding this subject, please do not hesitate to call our office.

Sincerely,

[Name of Office Manager or Physician]

Exhibit 4.17   Sample Deductible Letter

Dear [Patient Name]:

Your insurance company has processed your claim in the amount of $_____ for services we provided to you on _____. A portion of the reimbursement was used to satisfy your annual deductible of $ _____.

This means you are responsible for paying the first $_____ each year before your insurance begins making payments. You need to pay this amount to our office. This is shown on the enclosed Explanation of Medical [Medicare] Benefits stating the reimbursement paid by your insurance carrier to our office.

We appreciate your prompt attention to this bill. For your convenience, a return envelope is enclosed.

Sincerely,

[Name of Office Manager]

5 After Submission of Claims

Objectives

After completing this chapter, you should be able to:

- Understand third-party reimbursements
- Interpret EOBs and post payments
- Manage accounts receivable
- Understand how to handle difficult patient accounts

Introduction

After you submit a claim, you may need to follow it up to ensure that proper payment has been made by the patient's insurance company and that the patient's account was closed. To manage patient accounts and receive appropriate reimbursement for services rendered, your office staff must understand third-party reimbursements, how to interpret EOBs and post payments, how to manage accounts receivable, and how to handle difficult patient accounts. These "back office" functions of insurance processing challenge even highly experienced physicians and their staff.

Back office claim functions involve payment posting, account follow-up, rebilling of claims, accounts receivable management, and collections. The success of most back office functions relies heavily on the success of the front office functions of proper patient and insurance data collection, verification, and accurate coding and billing. As a founder of the Healthcare Financial Management Association stated, "The account of a patient properly admitted is already half collected!"

Understanding Third-Party Reimbursements

The amount a physician or patient is reimbursed for a service depends in part on the patient's insurance benefits. Traditionally, insurers reimburse on an 80/20 basis. That is, the insurance company pays 80 percent of its allowed amount for the service and the patient pays the remaining 20 percent as an out-of-pocket co-insurance.

The amount allowed for a service can vary from payer to payer, depending on the payer's reimbursement policy. For example, one payer may use a fee schedule, while another uses the UCR system. Fees you receive from HMO-, PPO-, or IPA-covered patients may be based on a contract or on a capitation basis. Medicare has its own separate fee schedule. Before an insurance company makes a payment, patients must usually meet their annual deductible.

The following examples illustrate reimbursement of two payers—a commercial carrier and Medicare.

Commercial Carrier Examples

1. Dr. Smith charges $200 for a specific procedure. The patient's insurance company allows $187 and pays 80 percent of the allowable, or $149.60. The patient has previously met his deductible and would thus be responsible for the difference (the co-payment). Payment would be as follows:

Dr. Smith's charge	$200.00
Insurance payment	$149.60
Patient co-insurance	$ 37.40 Amount due from patient $50.40
Balance billing	$ 13.00

   Dr. Smith is obligated to collect the full amount of her $200 charge.

2. Dr. Jones charges $50 for a service. The patient has not met his $250 annual deductible. The payer allows $48 for the service and reimburses on the 80/20 basis. Payment would be as follows:

Dr. Jones' charge	$ 50.00
Insurance payment	$ 0.00
Patient deductible	$ 50.00

   Because the patient has not met his deductible, in this example he is responsible for the entire payment.

3. Using example 2, if the patient had previously met his deductible, payments would be as follows:

Dr. Jones' charge	$ 50.00
Insurance payment	$ 38.40

| Patient co-insurance | $ 9.60 Patient responsibility is $11.60 |
| Balance billing | $ 2.00 |

Note: The insurance company pays 80 percent of the allowed amount, or 80 percent of $48.

4. Dr. Parsons provides a $100 service to a patient. The patient's insurance allows the full $100 and reimburses on the 80/20 basis. The patient has met her deductible. Payment would be as follows:

Dr. Parsons' charge	$100.00
Insurance payment	$ 80.00
Patient co-insurance	$ 20.00

In this example, the amount allowed by the insurance company is the same as the physician's charge.

5. Dr. Black charges $300.00 for a specific procedure. The contractual adjustment with the insurance company for this procedure is $120.00. Payment would be as follows:

Dr. Black's charge	$300.00
Insurance payment	$120.00
Patient payment	$ 0.00

Note: If the insurance company did not pay the contracted amount, a review letter should be sent for the additional amount.

Medicare Examples

Because Medicare reimburses on the basis of the Medicare Fee Schedule (MFS), charges and limits on charges are fixed. Physicians who participate in the Medicare program always accept assignment and agree to accept the MFS amounts for participating physicians as payment in full.

Nonparticipating physicians' fee schedule amounts are set at an amount 5 percent lower than those provided to participating physicians. However, if the nonparticipating physician does not accept assignment on a claim, the amount allowed by Medicare is 115 percent of that allowed if assignment had been taken.

Patients covered by Medicare must meet an annual outpatient deductible of $100. Medicare pays 80 percent of the allowed fee schedule amount, and the beneficiary is responsible for the remaining 20 percent co-insurance of the allowance. Medicare provides all physicians with fee schedules. If you have not yet obtained your fees from Medicare, contact your Medicare carrier.

1. Dr. Jones is *participating* with Medicare. She bills $125 for a service provided to a Medicare patient. The patient has previously met her deductible, and the MFS amount for the service is $100. Payment would be as follows:

Dr. Jones' charge	$125.00
Medicare payment	$ 80.00
Patient co-insurance	$ 20.00
Amount of write-off	$ 25.00

   Note: Dr. Jones can collect a maximum of $100 between the patient and Medicare, as $100 is the MFS amount. The difference, $25, would be written off of Dr. Jones' receivables. Also note that participating physicians are allowed to charge more than the fee schedule amount even though they may only collect the amount specified by the fee schedule.

2. Dr. Smith does *not participate* with Medicare, but is *accepting assignment* on the patient's claim. Although Dr. Smith normally charges $325 to commercial carriers for the service provided to the patient, the MFS limiting charge amount that applies to nonparticipating physicians for the service is $267.65. Thus, Dr. Smith can collect no more than $267.65 from the Medicare beneficiary. The patient has already met his Medicare deductible for the year. Payment would be as follows:

Dr. Smith's charge	$267.65
Medicare's payment	$214.12
Patient co-insurance	$ 53.53
Remainder	$ 0.00

3. Dr. Parsons is *not participating* with Medicare and *does not accept assignment* on a patient's claim. The patient has met her annual deductible. Dr. Parsons must restrict his charge for the service to the limiting charge amount provided on the MFS, $67.43. Medicare will allow for the service an amount equal to that given a nonparticipating physician who accepts assignment, or $58.63. Payments would be as follows:

Dr. Parsons' charge	$ 67.43
Medicare's payment	$ 46.91
Patient co-insurance	$ 20.52
Remainder	$ 0.00

Medicare will pay 80 percent of the allowed MFS amount. In this example, the patient is responsible for the difference between Dr. Parsons' charge and the amount of the Medicare payment. It is important to recall that Dr. Parsons had to limit his charge to $67.43—the MFS amount that a nonparticipating physician is allowed to charge for the service when not accepting assignment.

Interpreting EOB and Payment Posting

When payments are received in your office either from insurance plans or from patients, they must be posted to the patient's account. Insurance payments received through the mail are accompanied by an explanation of benefits (EOB). Payments from patients are received through the mail and at the time of their office visits. Payment posting will be done either on the computer or on the individual patient ledger cards if a pegboard system is used. A tracking system of accounts receivable (payments, contractual adjustments, write-offs), as well as carrier denials, needs to be maintained in order to monitor reimbursement patterns and trends.

Preposting Operations

Before posting an insurance payment to the patient's account, your practice must perform and document the following actions:

1. Compare the EOB with the original insurance claim, and review each carefully. All services reported on the claim form should be represented on the EOB. (**Note:** Some insurance EOBs list services by line item, while others provide a single line-item determination for all services.) Look for changes in CPT coding by the insurance company (for example, determine if a service was down-coded). The goal is to identify charges that can be appealed or rebilled for payment.

2. Investigate all denied services, determine the reason for the service denial, and appeal them, if appropriate. (Denials are usually indicated with zeros in the allowed amount or amount paid data field on the EOBs.)

3. Appeal all payment reductions based on the insurance's usual, customary, and reasonable (UCR) charge amount. Insurance companies utilize regional charge databases to inform a physician when the charge submitted exceeds the UCR norm. Unfortunately, the UCR data are often payer-specific, meaning that they are not the same for all insurers. Each insurance company has

its own UCR. The insurer will send a UCR letter explaining why the insurance company reduced the physician's fee and why the company feels it is too high for the practice area. Do not bill at each insurance UCR. Uniform billing should be done for each service to all carriers.

4. A carrier request for additional information that appears on the EOB must be addressed immediately. The goal is to get paid as quickly as possible by the insurance company. Each insurer also has a time limit on claim rectification.

The information contained on the EOB should be posted on the computer or manual patient ledger card promptly and carefully on receipt. An error in the posting process may cause the patient's account balance to be incorrect.

Tracking EOBs by carrier will help to monitor similar payments for similar procedures and diagnoses.

Contractual Adjustments

After the EOB has been carefully reviewed, the insurance payment should be posted to the patient's account. On the patient's account balance record, the office must account for the difference between the charge submitted on the claim and the amount allowed contractually, always specifically identifying in the patient record the type of adjustment made (for example, Medicare, HMO or PPO, professional courtesy, or a UCR reduction).

These types of adjustments generally are called *contractual adjustments*. A contractual adjustment is the difference between what a practice bills and what it is legally entitled to collect. For example, if a physician's normal fee is $1,200 and he or she signs with a PPO that has a contractual reimbursement of only $1,000 for the same service, the contractual adjustment would be $200. It is important to ensure that contractual adjustments shown on the EOB are in accordance with the contract. It is not uncommon to see contractual discounts taken in error.

Note: Never let your practice lump all adjustments into an account called *credit adjustments*. Specifically identifying contractual adjustments and other write-offs is critical to the management of a medical practice.

This information alerts a practice to which insurance programs are reducing charges the most. If the practice is writing off a large number of adjustments for a specific plan, the office should investigate and assess whether it makes sense to continue with the specific insurance plan. At the same time, the practice should determine if such write-offs are reasonable and, if so, whether or not they can be reduced. Specifically identifying write-offs is also a smart way to account for withhold adjustments made by managed care plans.

Withhold Adjustments

A withhold is an amount withheld from a physician's reimbursement that may or may not be reimbursed depending on the managed care plan's criteria for reimbursement. For example, if a physician's normal charge for a procedure is $1,000 and he or she signs a managed care contract that will only reimburse $800 for the same procedure, the managed care plan will approve $800 for payment and may subtract another 10 percent as a withhold adjustment. Therefore, the practice receives a check for $720 instead of $800. The $80 withheld should be accounted for separately in your office's computer or by means of other documentation if the practice is on a manual system.

At the end of the year, the practice should review how much was withheld by each managed care plan and then appeal for reimbursement of the withhold. If a plan will not reimburse the withhold, the office should have a representative of the plan explain the plan's withhold policy. It is preferable to have written criteria that describe the withhold and indications for withhold at the beginning of the contractual period. Reconfirm that there is no change at the anniversary of each contract period. If a particular plan will not reimburse the withhold, the practice must know the true discounted amount is not actually the approved amount but is also reduced by the plan withhold. An office should never write off a charge that has been denied by an insurance company until such denial has been fully investigated by office personnel.

Fractional Payment of the Allowed Charge

After taking into account contractual adjustments and other reductions, an insurance plan usually pays only a fraction of the allowed charge. Medicare, for example, pays 80 percent of the allowed amount. Some indemnity plans pay 90 percent. Your office should post the amount paid by the insurance plan to the patient's account in the computer or on a manual ledger account card. The balance of the account is the responsibility of the patient. The patient portion should be identified in their contract. It is important to know the patient responsibility before care is rendered.

If the balance is not paid, it should be billed in the next round of monthly statements. Therefore, your office needs to pay strict attention to the amount the patient is responsible for when posting insurance payments. This amount should be identified clearly when posting payment and contractual adjustments in the computer or on the patient's manual ledger account card. If errors are made during the posting process, the aging of accounts will be unreliable. Also, when patients' statements are mailed, they may contain incorrect balances due, which is guaranteed to upset patients. In most cases, the patients' insurance plans will also send them their own copies of the explanation of benefits for the patients' records.

Filing the Explanation of Benefits (EOB)

After the EOBs are posted, they should be filed with the respective copies of the insurance claim forms either in the patient's clinical file or in a separate business file set up for each patient. Some offices find it more efficient to maintain the EOBs in notebooks referenced by the insurance company. It is important for an office to keep the insurance claim forms and related EOBs together so that it can easily audit a patient's account history when such a need arises. In addition, a copy of the EOBs should be organized in a way that will allow someone to review them for consistency in payment on a periodic basis.

In the next chapter, we will discuss the importance and process of accounts receivable follow-up.

6 Insurance Accounts Receivable Management

Objectives

After completing this chapter, you should be able to:

- Understand what is important for accurate accounts receivable report preparation

- Recognize the use of the different types of accounts receivable follow-up letters to include:

  - Letter for claim inquiry on assigned claim

  - Letter for claim inquiry on unassigned claim

  - Letter to insurance commissioner

Introduction

While coding and billing are important to initiate the reimbursement process, tracking the amounts due your practice and payments received is critical to ensuring proper reimbursement. While verifying insurance information, determine if the deductible is met. Processing may be delayed in order to get other providers' (hospital) charges to apply to the deductible first. Having the ability to determine and separate accounts receivable (A/R) responsibility (that is, insurance and patient) will also help improve your practice's cash flow and overall accounts receivable reduction.

Keeping in mind that the goal of the A/R process is to collect the greatest amount from the insurance plan and patient in the shortest time period, to efficiently manage the accounts receivable process, practices need to:

- Develop a systematic process that defines all A/R collection activities by priority parameters and defined policies and procedures that can be implemented to resolve balances due

- Design A/R management reports using priority parameters for sorting reports, and provide relevant information for completing A/R tasks based on staff member responsibility

More simply put, design your reports so that your practice will receive the greatest benefit from their use in day-to-day A/R activities.

Accounts Receivable Report Preparation

Most computer billing systems provide practices with powerful A/R reporting capabilities, giving the practice the ability to generate A/R reports based on different selection criteria such as account numbers, patient name, aging of accounts (30, 60, or 90 days), account or insurance type, and balance due amounts. **Note:** Accounts that age more than 180 days have a very low eventual collection rate.

Unfortunately, the power of the reports themselves is often underutilized by the office staff, making the follow-up and collections process even more difficult to manage. Many practice A/R reports are sorted by patient account number or patient last name instead of by more effective priority parameters. Priority parameters represent the different categories or data fields available that can serve as the primary A/R sort specification.

Protocol should be determined for printing aging reports, and responsibilities should be assigned to appropriate staff members. Protocol for follow-up letters and when to send them to collection should also be established.

Instead of printing A/R reports by patient account number or name, practices should consider prioritizing accounts based on a combination of the following:

- Balance due (highest to lowest)
- Aging of account
- Account type, payer type, or insurance plan
- Financial responsibility (insurance versus patient)
- Date of claim submission or date of service

The reasons for prioritizing accounts are quite simple. First, because all practices have limited staff and practice management resources, they must consider the costs and benefits of all A/R activities. By focusing on the accounts with the highest outstanding balances as soon as possible, any problems with the claim can be identified and resolved through rebilling, thereby yielding a greater overall recovery. For example, some practices prioritize accounts in this way:

1. Greater than $3,000
2. $2,000 to $2,999

3. $1,000 to $1,999

4. $500 to $999

5. $100 to $499

6. $50 to $99

7. $10 to $49

Second, the longer an account remains in accounts receivable, the probability of collecting the full amount falls dramatically. According to industry collection studies, the collection recovery rate percentage by account aging is estimated as shown in Table 6.1.

Table 6.1   **Account Aging Percentages**

Current	60 days	90 days	180 days	220 days	Over 1 year
100%	90%	50%	30%	19%	11%

By sorting the A/R reports by account aging "buckets" (that is, 30, 60, 90, 120, etc.), the practice can focus on the account with the most outstanding days in aging. Some practices print separate A/R reports by aging category, such as those accounts for over 120 days, or from the "oldest" to "youngest" aging bucket.

Third, A/R problems are frequently based on similar circumstances caused by the type of account. For example, if the practice billed a wrong CPT code to Medicare for all patients, all beneficiary accounts affected will have A/R problems. So, to efficiently follow up with A/R problems and to follow up with as many similar account types as possible when communicating with a certain insurance type, the staff may want to organize the accounts into similar categories, account types, payer types, or specific insurance plans.

Fourth, identifying the reason for the A/R problem(s) may become more difficult because the practice cannot separate the patient responsibility from the insurance responsibility. This often occurs because insurance verification was not performed before services were rendered. If your A/R system can track and separate out insurance and patient responsibility by A/R report, seriously consider this option.

Now, consider how your A/R reports and your staff's A/R activities can be enhanced by simply resorting the way the A/R reports are printed. By combining any of the sort selections suggested above with increased collection efforts, your A/R will be well on its way below where it is today.

Most A/R report formats can be reprogrammed by either the office staff or software technical support group, to facilitate the practice's desire to recover more A/R. Large A/Rs may result in the need to borrow money to cover a cash flow deficit. The "time value" of money (how much it actually costs the practice) can be calculated by multiplying the amount owed by the days owed/365 multiplied by the passbook savings account. For example, if $100 is owed for 120 days at a passbook savings account of only 3 percent annually, the amount you have left, if collected today, is:

$$100 \times \frac{120}{365} \times 0.03 = \$0.99 \text{ or } 1\% \text{ of the total amount of the bill.}$$

If a practice grosses $300,000, that is a giveaway of at least $3,000 annually.

Follow-up of Unpaid Insurance Claims

The following general system can be used to collect on unpaid insurance claims.

Identifying Unpaid Claims

At least once a week the office should identify unpaid insurance claims that are at least 25 days old. The reason for starting at 25 days is that the office must find out as soon as possible whether claim forms were received by the insurance companies and entered into their computers. A chronic problem for many offices is that insurance companies will say they have no record of receiving claims.

By starting at 25 days, the office can refile claims early. Also, the sooner you start the follow-up process, the more quickly claims will be paid on balance. *A major goal of every medical practice is to obtain payment consistently within 30 to 45 days for all insurance claim forms filed.*

This is where the revised A/R report will help. Practices may also want to use the copy of the claims, which should have a centralized location, usually an alphabetized expandable file, for unpaid claims. Some offices may keep the office copies in patients' charts. Unless the office has access to a list of the unpaid claims, however, keeping the forms in the charts will often create inefficiencies. This is because the collection personnel will have to pull charts in order to follow up on accounts and will not know at any one time which claims are 25 days old.

Telephone Calls

For each claim at least 25 days old, the office should make a telephone call to each insurance company. This conversation must always be documented in the computer or some other location. Include the name of the contact at the insurance company, why the claim has not been paid, and when payment can be expected. If the documentation is made on paper, it should be attached to each office copy of the unpaid claim until payment is received. If the office files a large number of claims electronically, the forms can be attached to the computer edit report that lists the electronically filed claims.

Whether telephone calls should be made to every insurance company that has billings over 25 days old depends on how many claims are filed each week, how large the balances are, and the capabilities of the office's collection personnel. The goal of any office should be to try to make the phone calls.

"Tracer" Claims

If calls cannot be made or if communications with the insurance company fail, practices may want to use the tracer method. Tracer claims are a copy of the original claim form with the word "TRACER" stamped in red on it. The date of the tracer should also be written on the claim. These claims are then refiled with the respective insurance companies. A tracer designation indicates to most insurance companies that the office is inquiring about the status of an unpaid claim.

Refiling Claims—Rebilling

Depending on the follow-up call, the office should refile claims (via facsimile, if possible) or do whatever is necessary to get claims paid as quickly as possible. The practice's staff member who makes the calls must document who he or she talked to at the insurance companies. That way, the employee will have names of people to call back if the claims continue to be delinquent.

Insurance A/R Process Overview

As a summary of the insurance A/R process, the following steps may be taken to follow up previously submitted claims:

1. Contact the insurance company by phone on claims submitted at least 25 days ago.

2. Send a tracer claim or claim inquiry letter to the insurance company (assigned or unassigned).

3. After 40 days, contact the patient to inform him or her of problems and enlist his or her assistance.

4. Initiate telephone contact number two to the insurance company (claims submitted at least 50 days ago).

5. The patient becomes financially responsible for charges at 60 days. When billing the patient after 60 days, inform him or her of what and with whom contact has been made with the insurer.

6. Request a review and insurance appeal with documentation.

Sample Insurance A/R Follow-up Letters

Occasionally, insurance companies are slow to pay a claim. In these situations, you may want to consider inquiring about the status of the claim. For assigned claims, the practice may send a letter, similar to the sample letter shown in Exhibit 6.1.

In cases where an unassigned claim has been filed, the patient must make an inquiry to the insurance company. A letter from the patient to the slow-paying insurance company may help speed payment to the patient, which will in turn speed payment to your office. You may want to provide a letter, similar to the one shown in Exhibit 6.2, to the patient to send to the insurance company.

Use a letter to the insurance commissioner (Exhibit 6.3) after all your attempts to obtain payment from the patient's insurance company have failed. Check your state's insurance laws to determine *whether the patient or the physician has the jurisdiction to file the formal complaint* with the insurance commissioner.

Exhibit 6.1   **Sample Letter for Claim Inquiry on *Assigned* Claim**

Physician or Group Name

Address

Phone

Applicable Identification Number(s)

Insurance Carrier

Claims Processing Department

Address

RE: Patient's Name

Policyholder's Name

Policy Number

Patient's Identification Number

Dear Sir or Madam:

On [date], a claim was filed on behalf of the patient named above. To date, no payment has been received for this claim. We are requesting information regarding the following:

☐   Please verify amount of payment made to patient.

☐   Please review reimbursement due to under/overpayment of $_____.

Other: _____

Insurance Company Reply:

☐   Payment was made to patient in the amount of $_____ on _____.

Correct reimbursement should be $_____.

☐   Payment was made to your office on _____ for $_____.

☐   Other:

_____   _____   _____

Signature   Title   Date

Exhibit 6.2   **Sample Letter for Claim Inquiry on *Unassigned* Claim**

Patient's Name
Address
Phone Number

Insurance Company Name
Address

Attention: Supervisor of Claims Department

RE: Patient's Name
          Policyholder's Name
          Policy Number
          Patient's Identification Number

Dear Sir or Madam:

On [date] Dr [physician's name] of [include group or practice name, address, and applicable identification number], who is my physician, submitted an insurance claim for me in the amount of $_____ for my medical treatment. _____ weeks have passed and payment has not been received by me or my physician. Please check your records and contact me or Dr [physician's name] office immediately regarding this claim. I am anxious to settle this matter. Yours truly,

Patient's Name

Exhibit 6.3   Sample Letter to the Insurance Commissioner

Date

State Insurance Commissioner
Address
City, State, Zip Code

Dear Insurance Commissioner:

My physician filed the attached insurance claim form over thirty (30) days ago. Even after repeated attempts by my physician's office to contact the insurance company regarding the payment status of this claim, to this date my insurance company has not paid this claim and has provided no explanation to my physician for its nonpayment.

Please accept this letter as a formal written complaint against the insurance company. Your prompt attention to this matter would be greatly appreciated.

I am providing the insurance company and my physician with a copy of this notice.

Sincerely,

[Patient's Name]

pc: Practice Name
     Address

7 Requests for Review and Appeals

Objectives

After completing this chapter, you should be able to:

- Understand the purpose of appeals to insurance companies
- Understand the process of requesting a Medicare review
- Recognize the use of a letter to request a review

Appeals to Insurance Companies

It is essential that a medical practice's appeals to insurance companies be handled correctly. For Medicare and Medicaid plans, the carriers in each state have a specific methodology for appealing insurance claims. For other insurance carriers, submit appeals in writing. Your appeal letter should state clearly why the charge should be allowed and the medical necessity, if applicable. Attach documents that support your claim.

Periodically review a sample of your appeal letters to see how often and how quickly your office is paid after your appeals are filed. If reimbursements have taken a long time, the cause could be a poorly drafted appeal letter or your failure to include supporting documents. Never send an appeal letter that simply asks for a review of the denied or reduced charge. The letter must explain to the insurance company why the amount should be paid. Otherwise, the insurance company will assume it was correct in the first place in denying or reducing the charge. A letter asking only for a review is a waste of time; it will not result in a paid claim.

Medicare Requests for Review

Medicare has a formal administrative appeals process in which physicians and patients may challenge the determination of a claim. Most other insurance companies also allow for a review. Requesting a review is a simple process and very often results in a more favorable determination for you on a claim.

Some reasons why you may want to request a review are:

- The services were denied
- The services were down-coded to a lower level and paid at the lower level
- The allowed amount seems unreasonable or too low
- Other reasons, as appropriate

To request a review, you need to send a letter to the carrier requesting a review. Your letter should identify the claim you would like reviewed, and it should clearly state your reasons why you feel the determination should be changed. Include supporting documents you feel will help the reviewer see why the determination should be changed. Include information or explanations that were not included with the claim the first time it was submitted. This will help the reviewer see more clearly why the determination was incorrect the first time.

Part B Appeal Rights

As a provider of services to Medicare beneficiaries, you may appeal (request a review of) an initial claim determination if you:

- Accepted assignment on the claim; or
- Did not accept assignment on the claim, the claim was denied as not reasonable and necessary, and no waiver of liability was obtained from the beneficiary, thus requiring you to return to the beneficiary any money you had collected for that service; or
- Are acting as the duly authorized representative of the beneficiary.

If you are dissatisfied with the carrier's initial determination and the determination is subject to appeal, you may request a review. This request must be in writing, signed, and filed within six months of the date of the initial determination (date of EOB). Before requesting a review, check your explanation of benefits to determine (1) if the allowed amount shown for that procedure is the proper allowance for that service and (2) if rebundling and/or global surgery edits have been correctly applied. *The appeals process cannot resolve complaints with the Medicare Fee Schedule or with national policy decisions.* Appeals should be filed only on those claims in which you feel an error has been made or extenuating circumstances were overlooked.

If you remain dissatisfied after the review determination, and the amount in controversy is at least $100, you may request a fair hearing. Requests for fair hearings must be filed, in writing, within six months of the date of the review determination. You may request that a hearing be held in person or by telephone (allowing personal testimony), or "on-the-record" (based upon the information submitted with the request and information currently on file in the office). Please address these requests to the attention of the Hearing Department and indicate the type of hearing you prefer.

If your request for a hearing has not been acknowledged in writing within three weeks, you should send a second request. The regulations require that the carrier acknowledge receipt of hearings within 10 days. If you do not receive a timely acknowledgment, most likely it is because the carrier has not received your request.

If you are still dissatisfied with the determination made by the hearing officer, and the amount in controversy is at least $500, you may request a hearing before an administrative law judge of the Social Security Administration. The request must be in writing and filed within 60 days of the date of the carrier's fair hearing decision of record. If you are still dissatisfied, and the amount in controversy is at least $1,000, you may appeal to the Appeals Council. This is the highest level of administrative review before initiating judicial review.

For individual claims submitted by providers, physicians, and others who furnish items and services to Medicare beneficiaries, the responsibility for gathering and submitting documentation that supports claims and appeals rests with the provider. We will offer guidance and assistance as necessary, but the responsibility for identifying what is needed and where it is located is yours. Be specific in stating the reason for the appeal and send any supporting documentation.

Below is a list of documentation sources that have proven useful to providers.

X-ray reports

Test results

Medical history

Documentation of severity or acute onset

Consultation reports

Billing forms

Referrals

Plan of treatment

Nurse's notes

Ambulance trip sheets

Operative reports

Hospital progress notes

Copies of communications between physician and/or beneficiary, hospital, carrier, laboratory, etc.

A sample letter that you may use to request a review is shown in Exhibit 7.1.

Exhibit 7.1   **Sample Letter to Request a Review**

Insurance Company Name
Review Appeals Department
Address

RE: Patient's Name
        Policyholder's Name
        Contract or Policy Number
        Claim Number
        Submission Date

Dear Madam or Sir:

We are requesting a review of the above identified claim on behalf of your beneficiary. A signed authorization for release of information is enclosed, allowing you to correspond directly with our office regarding this claim.

In reviewing this claim, please consider the following facts and circumstances:

1.

2.

3.

4.

5.

(etc.)

The enclosed [consultation, laboratory, operative, etc.] report(s) support our position. We appreciate your prompt attention to this review.

Sincerely,

[Name of Physician]
[Identification Number(s)]

Appendix A

Glossary of Terms

The insurance processing industry has its own "language." The following glossary includes terms commonly used in the industry. Learning these terms will increase your understanding of the claims management process.

Accreditation—The process by which an outside, independent, impartial organization formally recognizes an institution as meeting predetermined standards set by that same organization.

Adjudicate—The processing of an insurance claim for coverage determination by an insurance company or agent.

Adjusted average per capita cost (AAPCC)—The estimated average fee-for-service cost of Medicare benefits for an individual by county of residence. It is based on the following factors: age, sex, institutional status, Medicaid, disability, and end-stage renal disease (ESRD) status. The Health Care Financing Administration (HCFA) uses the AAPCC as a basis for making monthly payments to managed care plans.

Allowable—The fee (the "approved amount") the third-party payer decides the physician should be paid for the services provided to a patient. The amount is usually the same as or lower than the physician's fee and serves as a payment baseline for adjudicating the claim.

Ambulatory patient groups (APGs)—A prospective payment system for the facility component of ambulatory care rendered in hospital ambulatory surgery, emergency department, and outpatient clinic settings.

Appeal—The request for review by a physician who questions the correctness of a health plan's reimbursement for services rendered. The physician usually appeals by sending additional information in the form of clinical or demographic information to clarify to the health plan and to receive appropriate reimbursement.

Assignment—An arrangement in which the policyholder designates that the physician receive the benefits (payment) for a claim. This differs from the usual procedure in which the person who has the insurance policy is the person who is to receive the benefits (payment) from that policy. Under assignment, in return for receiving direct payment from most third-party payers, the physician agrees to accept the third-party payer's allowable as the maximum amount that may be collected from the payer and patient for that claim.

Balance bill—The amount the physician collects from the patient, which is the difference between the physician's fee (the amount billed) for a service and the amount paid by a third-party payer. In some cases, the balance bill is limited to the difference between the third-party payer's allowable fee and the amount paid by the payer. If the physician accepts assignment of benefits, he or she may not bill the patient for the balance. Instead, the balance difference is not collected; the physician writes it off the books, and the patient is billed only for the amount of the co-payment, deductible, or co-insurance, as applicable.

Beneficiary—The person who "benefits" from having the insurance policy. Typically, this person is the patient, but it can also be a spouse or the parent or guardian of a child. Persons enrolled in the Medicare program are commonly referred to as beneficiaries.

Beneficiary appeal—A request by a Medicare beneficiary to have a health care decision altered or reversed.

Benefits—The amount payable by a plan to a provider, group, or hospital, as stated in the policy, toward the cost of a medical service.

Bundling—A payment that combines minor medical services or surgeries and principal procedures when performed together or within a specific period of time. Some governmental programs and insurance plans "bundle" the payment of the lesser service into the payment for the principal procedure.

Cap rate—The fixed prepaid amount of payment under capitation. Also known as capitation rate.

Capitation—A method of insurance reimbursement for professional services performed in which a provider is paid a fixed amount per patient for a defined time period (month or year) rather than a fee-for-service payment.

Case management—The process of managing the coordination and integration of a plan design through a patient care coordinator.

CHAMPUS/CHAMPVA—Civilian Health and Medical Programs of the Uniformed Services/Veterans Affairs, a government-sponsored health program for active-duty and retired personnel and their eligible dependents, and veterans.

Claim—The request for payment of a physician's fees (or of a hospital's fees) for services provided to patients.

Clinical Laboratory Improvement Act (CLIA)—This act regulates all laboratories that examine human specimens to provide information to assess, diagnose, prevent, or treat any disease or impairment. CLIA mandates that virtually all laboratories meet applicable federal requirements and have a CLIA certificate in order to receive reimbursement from federal programs.

Coding—The process of communicating to the third-party payers the services performed (CPT-4) and the diagnostic conditions (ICD-9-CM) treated using a standardized listing of alphanumeric codes.

Consultation—A type of physician evaluation in which one physician requests the opinion and advice of another physician in diagnosing or treating a patient condition. The consulting physician must communicate his or her findings to the requesting or attending physician. HCFA has established definitive criteria that define the parameters of a consultation.

Contract capitation—A per-member, monthly payment to a provider that covers contracted services and is paid in advance of the delivery of the service.

Contractual disallowance—The amount of a health care provider's charge that exceeds the contracted amount a health insurance plan has agreed to pay (allowance) that must be contractually adjusted from the patient's financial responsibility.

Coordination of benefits—An insurance policy clause that defines how the plan will reimburse for services when more than one insurance plan is applied to the claim for physician services; the process of adjudicating claims between two or more health insurance plans.

Co-insurance—The portion of the allowable the patient is responsible for paying to the provider. Most insurance policies have a 20 percent co-insurance but some have a 30 percent or 40 percent co-payment. The patient pays the physician the co-insurance percentage of the allowable fee, and the third-party payer pays the remaining percentage of the allowable fee.

Co-payment—The fixed portion of a visit that the patient is responsible for paying to the physician for each service provided. This is usually collected only in managed care plans. There may be a $5 to $10 co-payment for primary care visits, $10 to $15 co-payment for specialty visits, and a $5 to $15 co-payment for pharmacy, lab, or x-ray procedures. The co-payment is a fixed fee per visit, while the co-insurance varies with the cost of the procedure and is a percentage.

Coverage—The type and range of benefits—services, procedures, medical items, and so on—for which an insurance policy will pay. Coverage varies from payer to payer. It may include surgery or medical treatment of illnesses or injuries, emergency department care, and hospital services.

CPT—Physicians' Current Procedural Terminology, a systematic listing and coding of procedures and services performed by physicians. Each procedure or service is identified with a five-digit code.

Deductible—The amount the patient must pay "out-of-pocket" before insurance reimbursement starts. Usually calculated on an annual basis, the deductible can range from $100 to $5,000, depending on the insurance policy.

Diagnosis—The physician's classification of a patient's condition, sign, or symptom. Diagnoses are defined by the *International Classification of Diseases, Ninth Revision, Clinical Modification* (ICD-9-CM) coding system, Volumes 1 and 2.

Disallowance—The amount of a health care provider's charge that exceeds a health insurance plan's maximum allowable payment (allowance) or contracted payment as a percentage of provider-billed amount. Also referred to as disallowed amount, nonallowed amount, or contractual disallowance.

Encounter form—An itemized billing statement listing CPT and ICD-9-CM codes most often used by physicians to note diagnosis and treatment and related fees.

End-stage renal disease (ESRD)—A medical condition in which a person's kidneys have stopped functioning on a permanent basis, leading to the need for long-term dialysis and other medical services. Medicare beneficiaries with ESRD are not allowed to join managed care plans. If a Medicare managed care plan member later develops ESRD, he or she is allowed to stay in the plan.

Exclusive provider organization (EPO)—A health insurance plan similar to an HMO, but in which the member must stay within the provider network in order to receive benefits. EPOs are regulated under insurance statutes, not HMO legislation.

Employee Retirement Income Security Act (ERISA)—An act that places regulations on employee benefit plans, including health insurance. One of the provisions requires payers to send the member an EOB when a claim is denied. ERISA plan regulations supersede state plan regulations.

Established patient—A patient who has received professional services within the past three years from a physician or another physician of the same specialty (with the same billing number) who belongs to the same group practice.

Exclusion—A health insurance contract clause that defines conditions or treatments not covered by a health policy. Policy exclusions require practices to make patients aware of their financial responsibility for noncovered services through waiver of liability statements. Also called exceptions.

Explanation of medical benefits (EOMB)—The third-party payer report that explains the coverage and reimbursement determination for a claim or group of claims. Also referred to as EOB.

Federal Medicaid Managed Care Waiver Program—The process used by states to receive permission to implement managed care programs for their Medicaid or other categorically eligible beneficiaries.

Federal qualification—A status defined by the Tax Equity and Fiscal Responsibility Act (TEFRA), conferred by the Health Care Financing Administration (HCFA) after conducting an extensive evaluation of the managed care organization's structure and operations. An organization must be federally qualified or be designated as a health maintenance organization (HMO) or a competitive medical plan (CMP) to be eligible to participate in Medicare cost and risk contracts. Likewise, a managed care organization must be federally qualified or state plan defined to participate in the Medicaid managed care program.

Fee-for-service (FFS)—A billing and reimbursement method in which physicians charge for each medical service or unit provided to a patient.

Fee schedule—A list of charges or payments coded by procedure. Physicians have internal practice charge fee schedules, while Medicare has a payment fee schedule.

Fiscal soundness—The requirement that managed care organizations have sufficient operating funds on hand or available in reserve to cover all expenses associated with services for which they have assumed financial risk.

Flexible benefit option—An option that some Medicare managed care plans may offer that allows members to select additional benefits with a different payment structure.

Formulary—A list of selected pharmaceuticals and their appropriate dosages. In some managed care plans, providers are required to prescribe only from the formulary.

Gatekeeper—An arrangement in which a primary care physician serves as the patient's agent and arranges for and coordinates appropriate medical care and other necessary and appropriate referrals.

Global period—A defined period of time during which all medical services related to a similar condition or diagnosis are included in the payment for the initial surgery or treatment. Medicare sets global surgical periods (GSPs) from 0 to 90 days postoperatively.

Group or network model—A managed care organization model in which the managed care organization contracts with more than one physician group, and may contract with single and multispecialty groups that work out of their own office facility. The network may or may not provide care exclusively for the managed care organization's members.

Health Care Financing Administration (HCFA)–The administration that governs the financial affairs and operations of the Medicare and Medicaid systems for all health care providers.

HCPCS—Pronounced "hick-picks," a national coding system that provides a uniform method for health care providers to report professional services and supplies.

Health Employer Data and Information Set (HEDIS)—A standardized set of performance measures that assesses plans' performance on a number of elements, including financial stability, access, and quality of care. HEDIS enables purchasers and consumers to readily compare the performance of managed care plans. It has been used extensively by private sector purchasers to judge the quality of care provided by plans to their employees. It is sponsored, supported, and maintained by the National Committee for Quality Assurance (NCQA).

Health insurance claim form (also called HCFA-1500)—The most commonly used claim form for processing physician service billing. Last revised in 1992, the red-ink claim form is accepted by most insurance plans for processing claims.

Health maintenance organization (HMO)—A type of health insurance plan in which the physician is paid a capitated or fixed rate per month per patient enrolled in the practice. HMOs emphasize providing quality services while reducing utilization of specialists and increasing control of patient care by primary care gatekeepers.

Hospice—A medical and psychosocial program designed to provide for and relieve the suffering of terminally ill people. Medicare beneficiaries already enrolled in Medicare-certified hospice programs are not allowed to enroll in managed care plans. If a Medicare managed care plan member needs hospice care once already enrolled, he or she will be allowed to stay in the plan.

ICD-9-CM—A diagnostic code system based on the *International Classification of Diseases, Ninth Revision, Clinical Modification* (ICD-9-CM), Volumes 1 and 2, used in the United States. The ICD-9-CM coding system is maintained by the National Center on Vital and Health Statistics and HCFA. It differentiates diagnostic conditions and reflects care practiced, and is used by hospitals, governments, health insurance plans, and health care providers in the United States.

Indemnity plan—A traditional health insurance plan that reimburses the policyholder a defined amount or percentage for expenses from illness or accidents through fee-for-service. The most common indemnity plans pay 80 percent of total charges, leaving policyholders with a 20 percent co-insurance.

Individual practice association (IPA)—A type of health maintenance organization (HMO) that provides services through an association of self-employed physicians or physician groups who provide services in their offices, but negotiate contracts as a group of providers.

Insurance claim form—A reprinted form filed with a health insurance carrier that details the services provided and other pertinent data to receive benefit (payment).

Limiting charge—The maximum amount a nonparticipating physician can charge for services to a Medicare patient.

Managed care—A controlled method of delivering health care services in the most appropriate and cost-effective way. All care is managed, from managed indemnity to at-risk HMO care. The lower the premium, the more strictly the plan is managed. Many define this as PPO or HMO care. The purest definition is at-risk capitated care.

Managed care organization (MCO)—An entity that integrates financing and management with the delivery of health care services to an enrolled population. An MCO provides, offers, or arranges for coverage of designated health services needed by members for a fixed, prepaid amount. There are three basic models of MCOs: group or network model, individual practice association, and staff model.

Management services organization (MSO)—A management entity owned by a hospital physician organization or third party. The MSO contracts with payers, hospitals, and physicians to provide services such as negotiating fee schedules, handling administrative functions, billing, and collections.

Medicaid—A federal and state medical assistance program that provides basic health benefits for persons who cannot pay for them or are otherwise indigent.

Medical necessity–A process of determining the appropriateness and/or coverage of different health care treatments for specific diagnostic conditions based on insurance benefits and clinical guidelines. Also referred to as medically necessary.

Medicare—A federal health care program for people 65 or older and for people with conditions such as end-stage renal disease (ESRD). Coverage includes Part A inpatient hospital and Part B outpatient physician services.

Medicare carrier—A health insurance company that has been awarded a contract to serve as the government's administrative contractor to process and adjudicate claims under the Medicare Part B outpatient health program for beneficiaries in a defined geographic location, usually by state.

Medicare HMO—A managed care approach to Medicare. These plans use a limited network of health care providers and require prior approval from a primary care physician.

Medicare intermediary—A health insurance company that has been awarded a contract to serve as the government's administrative contractor to process and adjudicate claims under the Medicare Part A inpatient health program for beneficiaries in a defined geographic location, usually by state.

Medicare managed care—A health care option beneficiaries can choose to receive their Medicare benefits. Managed care plans have contracts with the government, specifically the Health Care Financing Administration (HCFA), to provide Medicare benefits. When a person enrolls in a Medicare managed care plan, he or she selects a physician from the plan's list of primary care physicians. This primary care physician is then responsible for coordinating all of the beneficiary's health care needs.

Medicare Part A—The part of the Medicare program that pays for hospitalization, home health care, care in a skilled nursing facility, and hospice care.

Medicare Part B—The part of the Medicare program that pays for outpatient hospital services, physician services, durable medical equipment, and other services and supplies.

Medicare risk—A contract between Medicare and a payer or between a payer and a provider in which the payer and the provider get paid a set amount, for a designated time period, for care of a patient base.

Medicare SELECT–Insurance coverage similar to Medicare supplemental insurance in most ways, but in which beneficiaries are obligated to use a network of health care providers contracted by the health insurer.

Medicare supplement—Private insurance coverage that pays the costs of services that are not covered by Medicare.

Medigap insurance—A plan offered by a private insurance carrier to supplement Medicare coverage.

Modifier—A two-digit alpha or numeric code used with procedure codes to provide additional clarification of the circumstances related to the provision of health care services. For example, CPT modifier -51—multiple surgical procedure is used with secondary surgical procedure codes to indicate that more than one procedure was performed by the same surgeon on the same day as another procedure.

National Committee for Quality Assurance (NCQA)—A nonprofit organization that evaluates and accredits managed care plans. It is also responsible for implementing the Health Employer Data and Information Set (HEDIS) data reporting system, which provides standardized performance measures for managed care plans (see HEDIS).

New patient—A patient who has not received any professional services within the past three years from a physician or another physician of the specialty who belongs to the same group practice or uses the same billing number.

Out-of-pocket expenses—Costs borne by the member that are not covered by the health care plan.

Part B premium—A monthly premium paid (usually deducted from a person's Social Security check) to cover Part B services in fee-for-service Medicare. Members of Medicare managed care plans must also pay this premium to receive full coverage and be eligible to join and stay in a managed care plan.

Participation—A contract between a physician and a third-party payer under which the physician agrees to accept assignment on all claims submitted to that payer. Participation contracts are often for a limited period of time, such as a year.

Peer review—Evaluation of the quality of the total health care provided by plan providers by equivalently trained medical personnel.

Per diem reimbursement—Reimbursement to an institution based on a fixed rate per day rather than on a charge-by-charge basis. There may be separate categories of per diem, for example medical, surgical, intensive care unit, etc., each with a different reimbursement.

Physician-hospital organization (PHO)—Hospital and medical staff (or an IPA) that provide services to patients and negotiate and obtain managed care contracts.

Place of service code—A series of standardized codes used by physicians to report the location where the health care services were provided (office, hospital, home, etc.).

Physician organization (PO)—A group of physicians banded together, usually for the purpose of contracting with managed care entities or to represent the physician component in a PHO.

Point of service (POS)—A plan in which members do not have to choose services (HMO versus traditional) until they need them.

Precertification—A method for preapproving all elective hospital admissions, surgeries, and other provider services as required by insurance carriers. Approval is essential before payment for services is received.

Preexisting condition—A physical condition that existed prior to the issuance of an insurance policy or enrollment in a managed care plan.

Preferred provider organization (PPO)—A managed care network of physicians and providers who agree to treat member patients at a discounted fee schedule.

Premium—The periodic payment (usually monthly) made by a policyholder to an insurance company to subscribe to a health insurance plan.

Prepayment—A method of paying for the cost of health care services in advance of their use.

Preventive health care—Health care that seeks to prevent the occurrence of conditions by fostering early detection of disease and morbidity and that focuses on keeping patients well in addition to healing them when they are sick.

Primary care physician (PCP)—The physician who serves as the initial contact between the member and the medical care system. The PCP is usually a physician, selected by the member upon enrollment, who is trained in one of the primary care specialties, and who treats and is responsible for coordinating the treatment of members assigned to his or her panel (see Gatekeeper).

Primary carrier/payer—The insurance carrier that pays benefits first when the patient has more than one insurance plan. The primary carrier is billed first.

Prior authorization number—The number assigned by a health insurance plan after the precertification approval process for treatment is completed.

Provider—The person or entity providing health care-related services, such as a physician or a hospital.

Provider number—A unique physician identification number (UPIN) assigned to a health care provider by insurance carriers and the government for accounting and tracking purposes.

Provider-sponsored organization (PSO)—A Medicare + Choice organization that is a public or private entity and is established or organized and operated by a health care provider or group of affiliated health care providers.

Referral—The introduction or transfer of a patient's care from one physician to another.

Reimbursement—Money paid by a third-party payer for a patient's medical bills.

Reinsurance—An insurance arrangement whereby the managed care organization or provider is reimbursed by a third party for costs exceeding a preset limit, usually an annual maximum. This is also called stop-loss coverage.

Risk adjustment—A system of adjusting rates paid to managed care providers to account for differences in beneficiary demographics, such as age, gender, race, ethnicity, medical condition, geographic location, at-risk populations (for example, homeless), etc.

Risk contract—A contract payment methodology between the Health Care Financing Administration (HCFA) and a managed care organization (HMO or CMP). This requires the delivery of at least all Medicare-covered services to members, as medically necessary, in return for a fixed monthly payment from the government and sometimes an additional fee paid by the enrollee. The managed care organization is then liable for those contractually offered services without regard to cost. (**Note:** Medicaid beneficiaries enrolled in risk contracts are not required to pay premiums.) Risk contracts may occur between any insurer and provider group. The group at risk accepts prepayment and is responsible for all contracted care.

Secondary carrier/payer—The insurance carrier that pays benefits after the primary insurance plan has paid first when a patient has more than one health plan.

Specialist physician—A physician who is certified to practice in a specific field, other than general or family practice, for example, cardiologist.

Staff model—A managed care organization model that employs physicians to provide health care to its members. All premiums and other revenues accrue to the managed care organization, which compensates physicians by salary.

Third-party payer—An entity, such as an insurance company, that has agreed via a contract (that is, the insurance policy) to pay for medical care provided to the patient. "Third-party" refers to the involvement of another entity besides the two parties directly involved in medical care, the patient and the physician. Third-party payer is frequently used interchangeably with insurance company, insurer, or payer.

Type of service code (TOS)—A code to be entered in block 24C of the HCFA-1500 form that defines the type of service provided—medical care, surgery, and so on.

UCR payment—An abbreviation for "usual, customary, and reasonable" payment. An amount paid by a health plan based on a combination of the physician's usual fee, the customary fee charged by physicians in a specific locality, and the reasonable fee for the service.

UPIN—The abbreviation for "unique physician identification number" used by Medicare for accounting and tracking physician services.

Utilization management—A process that measures the use of available resources to determine medical necessity, cost-effectiveness, and conformity to criteria for optimal use.

Utilization review—The process of examining health care services to measure medical necessity, quality of patient care, and the appropriateness of care to identify overuse or ineffective outcomes.

Withhold incentive—The percentage of payment held back by the insurer for a "risk account" in managed care HMO plans to cover unforeseen expenses. Withhold arrangements are used as an incentive for physicians to manage their utilization of higher-priced diagnostics and treatments with the potential for sharing profits (or losses).

Appendix B

Health Care Industry Associations and Publications

Associations

American Academy of Professional Coders (AAPC)
    2144 S. Highland Dr., Suite 100, Salt Lake City, UT 84106
    800 626-CODE

American Group Practice Association (AGPA)
    1422 Duke St., Alexandria, VA 22314
    703 838-0033

American Health Information Management Association (AHIMA)
    919 N. Michigan Ave., Suite 1400, Chicago, IL 60611-1683
    312 787-2672

American Medical Association (AMA)
    515 N. State St., Chicago, IL 60610
    800 621-8335 or 312 464-5000

Medical Group Management Association (MGMA)
    104 Inverness Terrace E., Englewood, CO 80112-5306
    303 799-1111

Physician Payment Review Commission (PPRC)
    2120 L St., N.W., Suite 200, Washington, DC 20037
    202 653-7220

Professional Association of Health Care Office Managers (PAHCOM)
    461 E. Ten Mile Rd., Pensacola, FL 32534-9714
    800 451-9311

Publication Sources

Advanstar Communications Inc.
    Publishes *Physician's Management*, a practice management magazine.
    7500 Old Oak Blvd., Cleveland, OH 44130
    216 891-2719

American Health Consultants Inc.
Publishes *Physician Payment Update, Physician's Marketing and Management,* and more than twenty newsletters relating to coding, reimbursement, management, and managed care.
P.O. Box 740056, Atlanta, GA 30374
800 688-2421

American Medical Association (AMA)
Publishes *CPT, Medicare RBRVS, CPT Companion, CPT Assistant, AM News,* and other newsletters and reference books on business and clinical subjects.
515 N. State St., Chicago, IL 60610
800 621-8335

Aspen Publishers Inc.
Publishes newsletters and reference books on a variety of health care management and reimbursement issues.
200 Orchard Ridge Dr., Suite 200, Gaithersburg, MD 20878
800 638-8437

Georgia Part B Medicare
Cahaba Government Benefit Administrators
12052 Middleground Rd., P.O. Box 3018, Savannah, GA 31402-3018

Harcourt Brace Professional Publishing
Medical Practice Management Handbook for CPAs
6277 Sea Harbor Dr., Orlando, FL 32887-4600
800 831-7799

Healthcare Management Advisors Inc.
Provides education and technical support in the areas of clinical data quality, practice improvement and regulatory compliance for physicians, hospitals, and other health care providers.
11940 Alpharetta Hwy., Suite 150, Alpharetta, GA 30004
800 875-8462

Medical Economics Publishing
Publishes *Medical Economics,* a practice management magazine (24 times a year).
5 Paragon Dr., Montvale, NJ 07645-1742
800 432-4570

Medical Office Manager
Publishes *Medical Office Manager,* a practice management newsletter.
P.O. Box 52843, Atlanta, GA 30355
404 369-8105

Medicode

 Publishes and distributes practice management reference resources.

 5225 Wiley Post Way, Suite 500, Salt Lake City, UT 84116-2889

 800 999-4600

Moorhead Publications

 Publishes *Physicians and Computers* magazine.

 810 S. Waukegan Rd., Suite 200, Lake Forest, IL 60045

 847 615-8333

Opus Communications

 Publishes practice management newsletters such as *Briefings in Practice Management.*

 P.O. Box 1168, Marblehead, MA 01945

 617 639-1872

Practice Management Information Corporation (PMIC)

 Publishes and distributes practice management reference resources.

 2001 Butterfield Rd., Suite 850, Downers Grove, IL 60515

 800 633-4215

St. Anthony Publishing

 Publishes coding reference guides and newsletters for a variety of specialties.

 P.O. Box 96561, Washington, DC 20090

 800 632-0123

United Communications Group

 Publishes *Part B-News, Medicare Compliance Alert,* and other newsletters dealing with coding and reimbursement issues.

 11300 Rockville Pike, Suite 1100, Rockville, MD 20852

 800 929-4824

Index

Page numbers in **boldface** refer to entries in the glossary.

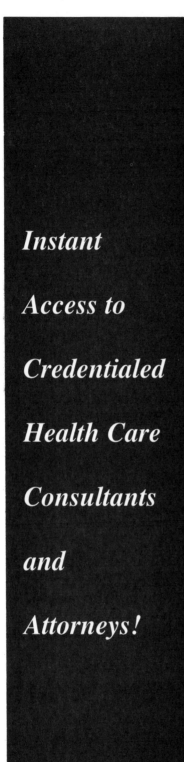

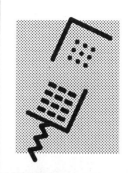